SLIMMERS
COOKBOOK

CAVENDISH HOUSE

SLIMMERS COOKBOOK

Contents

Published by
Marshall Cavendish Limited
58 Old Compton Street
London WV1 5PA

© Marshall Cavendish Limited 1980-83

ISBN 0 85685 718 1
Printed in Yugoslavia

Contributors:
Patricia Davies
Rose Elliot
Stella Henvey
Lesley O'Malley
Susan Rowley
Elizabeth Seldon

Front cover photographs:
Left, Colour Library International
Top right, Roger Phillips
Bottom right, Alan Duns

Back cover photograph:
Roger Phillips

Credits
Page 1: china 'Lunaville' available at Liberty, Regent St, London W1. **Pages 10/11:** china and glass at Harvey Nichols, Knightsbridge, London SW1. **Pages 14/15:** china and cutlery by Denby available at John Lewis, Oxford St, London W1. **Page 20:** copper gratin dish at "Copper shop", Neal St, London WC2. **Page 30:** Laura Ashley print china available at Dickins & Jones, Regent St, London W1, fabric at Laura Ashley, Sloane St, London SW1. **Page 41:** purple china at Liberty. **Page 42:** picnic basket and equipment all at John Lewis. **Pages 45/47:** china, glasses, cutlery and napkins all available at John Lewis. **Pages 46/48:** fish plat at David Mellor Sloane Sq, London SW1, white china at General Trading Co, Sloane St, London SW1. **Page 50:** glass bowl on pedestal at David Mellor. **Page 52:** china at John Lewis. **Page 59:** glasses at David Mellor.

Introduction

Who needs a cookbook when they're slimming?

Anyone who wants to enjoy good food while losing weight . . . anyone who wants to eat well with their family and friends, without putting on pounds. That's why we've produced a cookbook that makes it easy to keep an eye on your own diet *and* to cook creatively.

All the recipes are specially worked out for you to use as part of either a low-Calorie, or a low-carbohydrate, diet. These are two well-recognized methods of losing weight; both are equally effective but we've explained the differences so that you can choose the type of diet which suits you best. Every recipe in the book is given a Calorie as well as a carbohydrate count and, for extra help in planning your diet, there is a comprehensive chart listing the carbohydrate and Calorie content of the most common foods.

Slimmers' Cookbook caters for your complete range of cooking and entertaining needs. If you're eating alone there are plenty of tasty recipes for one. For those with a family to feed there are appetizing three-course meals, continental-style dishes and picnic fare. When cooking for guests, turn to our specially-chosen menus: they show you how to entertain with style and flair—without saying goodbye to a good figure.

Roger Phillips

SUCCESSFUL SLIMMING

Sensible slimming is all about eating the right kinds of food and in the right quantity. A thoughtfully chosen, well-balanced diet will provide the nutrients you need for good health, satisfy your appetite and help you slim.

There are all sorts of reasons *why* people become overweight, but *how* they do so is simply by eating more than they really need. This 'extra' is stored by the body as fat.

The only way to lose weight is by using up this store, and this is done by being both more active and more careful about food. It is choice of food that this book is concerned with, for diet is, basically, a method of regulating the amount and type of food eaten.

For many people, however, dieting and being overweight become a vicious circle. They adopt a diet to lose a few layers of flab and after a while, when the battle is won, they abandon it and return to the old eating habits that caused the flab in the first place.

It's important to break that vicious circle. Since dieting, particularly in the early stages, requires a degree of willpower, it is only sensible to choose a method you will find relatively easy to stick to. There are two well-recognized weight-reducing diets—the low-Calorie method and the low carbohydrate method. Both are equally effective, provided they are followed scrupulously. Choose the method you think will suit you best and give it a fair trial for at least one month.

Remember, however, that anyone who follows a diabetic diet will need specialized advice before embarking on a slimming campaign.

If you have quite a bit of weight to lose, you will, once you start to diet, lose water as well as fat. This is because stored carbohydrate 'holds' a certain quantity of water. After a while you will not lose quite so much water, but you will continue to use up your fat store at a steady pace. Do not be discouraged because your rate of weight loss has slowed down; from then on you are actually losing fat and only fat. At this stage a weight loss of 450–900 g [1–2 lb] a week indicates excellent progress.

The right kind of diet is not a fad—it is a way of life. It should comprise all the food you need for good health, food you can afford, food that is easy and convenient to prepare and, above all, food you will enjoy.

As well as making you fitter and more shapely, the right diet should get you into a good eating pattern which is so comfortable you will not wish to return to your former habits. It is not just the figure that suffers from a poorly balanced diet; your general health is also affected.

Because it is important to maintain good health as well as a good figure, we have to know about foods and their constituents and which will provide our body with all the nutrients that it needs.

Proteins are the 'body builders'. We all need a regular supply of protein and an extra helping during growth and pregnancy. Protein-rich foods are meat, eggs, milk, fish, cheese, wheatflour and soya. High-protein foods can compensate for the reduction of fats and carbohydrates in a diet, but nothing can replace protein.

Paul Williams

Carbohydrates comprise the sugars and starches in food. When food containing carbohydrates (such as bread, pasta, cereals, potatoes, nuts and fruit) is eaten, it is broken down during the digestive process into glucose. This circulates in the blood stream, providing energy to all parts of the body.

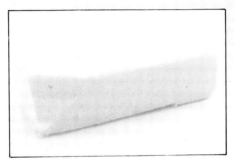

Fats also provide us with energy. High-fat foods are the fats themselves—lard, suet, dripping, oil, butter and margarine. Other foods containing a lot of fats are certain cuts of meat, bacon, dairy produce (particularly butter and cheese), pastry (especially flaky pastries) and nuts.

Frederick Mancini

Vitamins and minerals are required for good health, clear skin, sparkling eyes, shining hair and strong bones and teeth.
●Vitamin A is found in liver, kidney, oily

fish, egg yolk, dark green leafy vegetables, carrots, tomatoes and dried apricots.
●Vitamin B is obtained from meat (especially liver), wholemeal bread, milk and green vegetables.
●Vitamin C is present in most fresh fruit and vegetables. The richest sources are citrous fruit, blackcurrants, strawberries, melon, cabbage and Brussels sprouts.
●Vitamin D can be manufactured in the body by the action of sunlight on the skin. The best dietary sources are liver, oily fish, eggs, margarine and milk.
●Calcium is supplied by milk, yoghurt and cheese.
●Iron is obtained from meat, liver, spinach, kale, pulses, egg yolk, dried fruit and bread.

Roughage aids good digestion. Foods which are high in roughage or fibre—notably wholemeal bread and pasta, wholegrain cereals, raw vegetables and fruit—contain cellulose and other complex carbohydrates which are not broken down during the digestion process. This bulky material adds volume and weight to food and helps its passage through the digestive tract.

Water is of vital importance to us. In non-tropical climates at least one litre [two pints] of water should be drunk each day. This may be consumed in the form of coffee, tea or other drinks.

The balance of water in the body is usually carefully regulated, but day-to-day fluctuations do occur. For this reason, it is best to weigh yourself only once a week, at the same time and preferably in the same clothes.

THE LOW-CALORIE SLIMMING METHOD

Basically, a Calorie is a measure of the amount of energy a food will supply. If the food we eat supplies us with more energy, or Calories, than we burn up in our daily activities, then the surplus is stored in our body as fat.

Cutting Calories

On a low-Calorie diet, you reduce your daily intake of Calories and draw instead on your fat reserves for the energy you need. 'Spending' Calories by being more active physically also helps.

All food supplies Calories—there is really no such thing as a 'slimming food' or a 'fattening food'. But some foods supply, weight for weight, more Calories than others.

On a low-Calorie diet it is high-Calorie foods which are restricted. The chart at the back of the book gives the Calorie content of different foods. Broadly speaking, sugary foods, such as cakes, biscuits, jam and other preserves as well as sugar itself, are severely restricted or forbidden, and so are alcohol and syrupy drinks. These are all 'empty' foods, supplying little or nothing in the way of food value, but loaded with Calories. In addition, rich fatty foods—cream, buttery sauces, oily dressings and fats and oils themselves—are restricted.

On the other hand, you are encouraged to eat plenty of fresh fruit, salad stuffs, yoghurt and cottage cheese. Also, vegetables, white fish, lean meat and eggs (provided they are cooked with little or no fat). Bread, pasta and cereals (preferably whole grain) as well as cheese are allowed in moderation.

Counting Calories

Generally speaking, women leading a moderately active life require about 1,800–2,200 Calories per day to keep their weight steady. Men require about 500 Calories more.

Reducing your daily Calorie intake to 1,500 Calories a day will produce a steady, gradual weight loss.

If you have only a little weight to lose, or if you have just decided to start slimming, you may prefer to cut down a little more for quicker results. In this case, somewhere around 1,000 Calories per day could suit you better. It is not advisable to diet at the lower level for more than a short time without consulting your doctor.

It is helpful to remember that dieting can be flexible. For example, you can adopt a 1,000 Calorie diet on Monday and a 1,500 Calorie diet on Tuesday. The effect is the same as following a 1,250 Calorie diet each day.

Ground rules

● Whichever method you choose, you must calculate the 'cost' of every single thing you eat and drink during the day—either in Calories or in carbohydrate units.
● Never mix the two methods. If following a low-Calorie slimming plan, ignore the carbohydrate unit count and vice versa.

THE LOW-CARBOHYDRATE SLIMMING METHOD

The carbohydrate value of food is calculated by the amount of sugar, starch and dextrin it contains. If we consume more carbohydrate than we need, the excess glucose goes to the liver where it is turned into fat and then stored around the body.

The low-carbohydrate method concentrates on reducing the intake of carbohydrate food. Many people find this more convenient than following a Calorie-controlled diet—there is no need to painstakingly weigh every single item of food, nor do you need to carry around a pocket calculator to work out its Calorific value. Instead, you quickly learn which foods to avoid and which you can eat in moderation.

Cutting carbohydrates

The chart at the back of the book gives the carbohydrate unit content of different food. As a guide, starchy food, such as bananas, bread, baked beans, dried fruit, chocolate, pasta, potatoes, rice and thickened soups are restricted. Also, sweet alcoholic drinks.

Sugar is pure carbohydrate so cakes, ice-cream, jams, chocolate and sugar itself are out.

But you are allowed fats in moderation, and a little dry wine or tot of spirit.

Counting carbohydrates

Counting carbohydrate units is easier than counting Calories as you are dealing with smaller figures.

Cutting your intake of carbohydrates to 15 units a day will result in a gentle but sure weight loss. For quicker results, stick to only ten carbohydrate units a day. Reducing your intake below this level is not recommended.

FAT-FIGHTING COOKERY

The way you prepare and cook food is just as important as the choice of food itself.

Grill rather than fry every time.
● A grill pan fitted with a wire rack is best—fat can drip into the base of the pan and be discarded.
● When grilling fish or very lean meat, use a pastry brush to add the lightest touch of oil to prevent the food drying out or burning. Preheat the grill before you place food under

it, then brown it quickly on both sides. (This seals in nutrients and flavour. It also prevents any added oil from seeping into the food.) Reduce the heat to moderate and grill slowly until cooked through.

Shallow frying: if you must fry, use a non-stick pan and a smear of oil.
● There's no need to add any oil or fat to mince, bacon or sausages as these can cook in their own fat—just start them over low heat so that their fat will run.
● Drain off all excess fat from the pan before adding other ingredients.
● Drain shallow fried food on absorbent kitchen paper before serving.

Stews and casseroles: instead of pre-frying meat and vegetables, use the cold-start method (ideal for cheaper cuts of meat). Simply cover the food with cold stock or water, then bring to simmering point.
● Use cornflour rather than plain flour for thickening—you need half as much cornflour to do the job.
● Dried onion flakes, mixed vegetables and peppers act as thickening agents because they absorb some liquid as they reconstitute.

● Trim meat of all visible fat before cooking. Always skim the surface of home-made stock when it has cooled. If cooking a casserole in advance, skim off fat before re-heating; if serving the dish straight away, use a baster to remove droplets of fat which rise to the top.

Vegetables: never fry vegetables for they absorb a lot of fat. Eat them raw, lightly boiled, steamed or braised instead.
● Use low-fat slimmers' spread in place of butter for glazing vegetables.
● Use left-over vegetable purées for thickening sauces and soups.

Desserts: end meals with fresh fruit instead of sticky confections.
● Whisk as much air as possible into mousses and whips. This way your slimmer's portion will seem more.

Fruit salad with yoghurt is a healthier and less fattening snack for Calorie-counters than sweet creamy coffee and doughnuts. Similarly, carbohydrate-counters would be better off renouncing a Spotted Dick-type dessert in favour of cheese and biscuits.

David Levin

PLANNING YOUR DIET

Calculating the calorific value of foods when you are not used to it can be complicated. You may get so Calorie or carbohydrate unit minded that your diet is short of essential nutrients. By eating a balanced, varied diet and concentrating on food which supply proteins, vitamins and minerals, you are assured of the vital nutrients for good health.

Now you know all the facts about slimming it's time to work out which slimming plan is best for you.

You can be your own dietitian, provided you are prepared to be really honest with yourself. Think back to a typical weekday and an average weekend day and carefully write down every single item of food and drink you had on those days. Try to remember everything—spoonfuls of sugar, any snacks or nibbles. It really is not worth cheating—no one else is going to see the list, so you will only be fooling yourself.

Now, examine the list critically and make a note of the way in which you cook, how your social life affects your eating habits and how often your favourite foods appear. Then, using the Calorie and carbohydrate unit chart at the back of the book, work out the content of every item on your list so you can see where excessive units are coming from.

You have to decide how to deal with that excess. If, for example, you favour fried and fatty foods, then you could follow the low carbohydrate diet which allows these in moderation. Alternatively, you could choose a Calorie-controlled diet which reduces these foods to a minimum. The first choice enables you to

continue enjoying your favourite food and shed weight gradually. The second is likely to result in quicker weight loss—but will be harder to stick to.

Now analyse your eating habits. It doesn't really matter if you are not a breakfast eater—provided you do not later tuck into a chocolate bar which provides energy, but no food value.

If you omit breakfast, and eat only two meals a day, make sure that each one contains protein-rich food (meat, fish, egg or pulses) and includes a portion of fresh vegetables or fruit.

The kind of life you lead will, obviously, affect the way in which you organize your meals. If, for example, you have to snatch a quick office lunch then you will have to plan in a different way than if you are at home during the day with the refrigerator and larder readily accessible. Whatever your lifestyle, there is a section in this book for you with recipes already Calorie and carbohydrate counted to make the going easy.

Boredom can be one of the slimmer's greatest pitfalls. So, four basic recipes, which will help ring the changes, have been included here:
Tomato sauce (page 13)
Egg sauce (page 12)
Buttermilk dressing (page 11)
Mock hollandaise sauce (page 8)

When you have become accustomed to weighing out all the foods you eat and to calculating their Calorie and carbohydrate content then you can begin experimenting with your week's total according to your lifestyle and circumstances. You will find that your slimming efforts will benefit from a flexible approach to eating. The menus and recipes which follow have been prepared to help adopt this approach.

Whichever diet you decide to follow, you will have all the nutrients you need at each meal with the addition of vegetables or fruit of your choice. So, do not put off starting to slim until tomorrow, next week or after the holidays—by then you may have even more weight to lose.

Frederick Mancini

Five meals a day
on 1500 Calories or 15 carbohydrate units

Here is a meal plan designed for those who prefer to eat several small meals during the day, rather than three large ones. Sticking to this sort of intake each day will ensure a gentle, but steady weight loss.

The milk included can be taken on its own or in tea or coffee if wished but artificial sweetener, not sugar should be used.

With the exception of the tomato mould, the first four suggestions on each list can be prepared for one person. The fifth meal caters for four so you can feed non-slimmers in the evening without straying from your diet. If following the low-carbohydrate diet, serve the remaining tomato mould to non-slimmers as the first course preceding the kidney and mushroom casserole.

FIVE MEALS A DAY ON 1,500 CALS OR 15 CU				
Low-Calorie	**Cals**	**(CU)**	**Low-carbohydrate**	**CU** **(Cals)**
MEAL 1: **Complete meal muesli**	170	(3½)	MEAL 1: Fresh fruit cocktail: ½ grapefruit, 1 orange, —garnish with mint	2 (60)
MEAL 2: Cerises Suisse (page 39) 1 crispbread	160	(2½)	MEAL 2: **Egg Benedict** 1 crispbread	½ (415)
MEAL 3: Open sandwiches: arrange lettuce, tomato, cucumber, watercress and spring onion on 2 large slices thinly buttered wholemeal bread; moisten with 15 ml [1 tbs] slim- line salad cream. Then top with 50 g [2 oz] sliced chicken OR 25 g [1 oz] Edam OR 75 g [3 oz] prawns	335	(10)	MEAL 3: Tomato mould (page 57) Salad special: mix 100 g [¼ lb] cottage cheese with 2 sticks chopped celery; place on a bed of lettuce and top with sliced chicken OR grated Edam OR prawns, moistened with blender mayonnaise (page 48)	1 (440)
MEAL 4: **Glory yoghurt**	170	(2½)	MEAL 4: **Minty yoghurt cooler**	½ (115)
MEAL 5: Fresh vegetable cocktail (page 58) **Kidney and mushroom casserole** **Cabbage and green pepper salad** Apricot mousse (page 56)	480	(10)	MEAL 5: **Kidney and mushroom casserole** **Cabbage and green pepper salad** Apricot mousse (page 56)	8½ (450)
EXTRA: 275 ml [½ pt] milk	185	(2½)	EXTRA: 275 ml [½ pt] milk	2½ (185)
Total:	**1,500**	**(31)**		**15 (1,665)**
Recipes in bold are given in this chapter.				

Glory yoghurt

❌ *One of the secrets of successful slimming is to take trouble over the presentation of foods so that mealtimes remain something of an occasion. Simple ingredients, put together carefully and served in a tall glass with a long spoon produces a dish that looks far more Calorific than it is and will make any slimmer feel quite self-indulgent—all good slimming psychology! Serve the second portion to a child.*

Slimmer's portion:
Calories: 170
Carbohydrate units: 2½

SERVES 2
1 medium-sized banana
**125 ml [4 fl oz] low-fat
 raspberry, strawberry or
 black cherry yoghurt**
**125 ml [4 fl oz] low-fat natural
 yoghurt**
**15 g [½ oz] toasted and
 chopped hazelnuts**

1 Peel the banana then slice thinly.

2 Spoon a little of the flavoured yoghurt into the bottom of two tall glasses, then add some banana slices. Top with a layer of natural yoghurt followed by more of the fruit yoghurt. Continue in this way until all the ingredients are used up.

3 Sprinkle the nuts over and serve at once.

Variations
Other combinations of fruit and flavoured yoghurt can be used:
● For blackcurrant and pear glory, omit the banana and use a large, ripe pear instead. Remove the core (and skin if tough) then cut into small pieces. Layer with low-fat blackcurrant flavoured yoghurt and plain yoghurt. Pour over 15 ml [1 tablespoon] blackcurrant syrup.
　Calories: 165
　Carbohydrate units: 1½
● For minty yoghurt cooler, peel, cube and then liquidize 350 g [¾ lb] cucumber with 225 ml [8 fl oz] low-fat natural yoghurt and 2 sprigs of fresh mint. Season to taste with salt. Serve well chilled and garnished with mint.
　Calories: 115
　Carbohydrate units: 1

Mock hollandaise sauce

This sauce is strictly for those following a low-carbohydrate diet and, of course, for non-slimmers. It is excellent served with plain grilled fish or steak or even over plain boiled green vegetables. See also Egg Benedict, right. Once blended, the sauce can be kept in a plastic screw-top container in the refrigerator for up to a week. It can then be warmed as required.

Do not worry if the sauce looks curdled after blending—it will become smooth when heated.

Slimmer's portion, serving 4:
Calories: 270
Carbohydrate units: 0
Slimmer's portion, serving 6:
Calories: 185
Carbohydrate units: 0

MAKES 4–6 SERVINGS
100 g [¼ lb] butter
3 medium-sized egg yolks
15 ml [1 tablespoon] lemon juice
pinch of salt
pinch of cayenne pepper

1 Leave the butter to soften at room temperature.

2 Put the softened butter, egg yolks, lemon juice, salt and cayenne pepper into a liquidizer with 15 ml [1 tablespoon] hot water and blend thoroughly.

3 Prepare a double boiler. Set over low heat and pour the blended mixture into the top half of the boiler. Heat, stirring constantly, for about 10 minutes until the sauce thickens and becomes smooth. Be careful not to overheat or the sauce will curdle. Serve immediately.

Egg Benedict

This is a very rich snack meal for the low-carbohydrate slimmer. The recipe for mock hollandaise sauce is given left. Low-calorie slimmers could substitute 15 ml [1 tablespoon] soured cream for the hollandaise sauce in this recipe and reduce the Calorie content to 240. For a more substantial meal, poach two eggs, use a larger portion of hollandaise sauce and serve with a plain green salad or a lightly-boiled green vegetable.

Slimmer's portion:
Calories: 385
Carbohydrate units: 0

SERVES 1
1 medium-sized egg
50 g [2 oz] sliced lean ham
1 small portion prepared mock hollandaise sauce

To garnish:
watercress

1 Turn the grill on to moderate heat.

2 Poach the egg, following the method on page 15.

3 While the egg is cooking, heat the ham under the grill but do not allow it to brown. Heat the hollandaise sauce. Place the ham on a plate. Slip the drained poached egg on to the ham and spoon over a little of the warm hollandaise sauce.

OR remove the ham from under the grill and slip the egg on to the centre. Spoon over a little of the cold hollandaise sauce. Return to the grill and heat gently until the sauce is bubbling and hot.

Complete meal fruit muesli

Although this muesli might seem quite high in Calories, it is very filling and nourishing and makes a complete meal in itself. According to the originator of muesli, Dr. Bircher Benner, the entire apple should be used, including skin, core and pips.

Calories: 170
Carbohydrate units: 3½

SERVES 1
75 ml [3 fl oz] low-fat natural yoghurt
2.5 ml [½ teaspoon] clear honey
15 g [½ oz] rolled oats
2.5 ml [½ teaspoon] wheatgerm
1 small dessert apple
10 ml [2 teaspoons] toasted hazelnuts, chopped

1 Mix the yoghurt together with the honey, oats and wheatgerm.

2 Grate the apple coarsely, including the skin and as much of the core as possible. Add to the yoghurt mixture and stir well to mix.

3 Sprinkle the toasted nuts over and eat immediately.

Variation

● For buttermilk and banana muesli, replace the yoghurt with 75 ml [3 fl oz] buttermilk; mix with 15 ml [1 tablespoon] raisins, the oats and wheatgerm. Omit honey. Peel and mash 1 small banana; mix into buttermilk mixture. Sprinkle hazelnuts over.
Calories: 195
Carbohydrate units: 8

Frederick Mancini

Cabbage and green pepper salad

When making salads for slimmers, it is particularly important to pay attention to the combination of ingredients because the slimmer does not have the advantage of a tasty vinaigrette dressing. In this salad, the green pepper, celery and apple give a lovely flavour, while the orange juice keeps the mixture deliciously moist.

Slimmer's portion:
Calories: 80
Carbohydrate units: 2

SERVES 4
450 g [1 lb] white cabbage
175 g [6 oz] green pepper
4 celery sticks
100 g [¼ lb] carrots
2 medium-sized dessert apples
60 ml [4 tablespoons] orange juice
salt
freshly ground black pepper

1 Wash the cabbage, then shred it very finely or grate it fairly coarsely.

2 Core and de-seed the pepper, then chop finely. Scrub, then chop the celery and carrots. Core, then dice the apples. Mix together with the cabbage, then add enough orange juice to moisten. Season to taste with salt and pepper.

Kidney and mushroom casserole

Kidneys are rich in B-group vitamins as well as iron and other minerals. Serve this casserole with cabbage and green pepper salad and, if wished, for the non-slimmers, creamed potatoes.

Slimmer's portion:
Calories: 255
Carbohydrate units: 1½

SERVES 4
8 lambs' kidneys
1 large onion
175 g [6 oz] button mushrooms
175 g [6 oz] tomatoes
15 ml [1 tablespoon] vegetable oil
salt
freshly ground black pepper
chopped parsley to garnish

For this nutritious meal, Calories total only 365; carbohydrate units 42. Tomato mould (page 57) is followed by kidney and mushroom casserole with cabbage and pepper salad.

1 Heat the oven to 180°C [350°F] gas mark 4.

2 Skin and core the kidneys then chop into even-sized pieces. Peel and chop the onion; wipe and slice the mushrooms and skin and chop the tomatoes.

3 Heat the oil in a medium-sized, ovenproof casserole. Add the onion and fry over a low heat for 5 minutes without browning, then add the mushrooms and fry for a further 1–2 minutes.

4 Add the kidneys to the saucepan, increase the heat and cook the kidneys quickly until lightly browned. Then stir in the tomatoes and salt and pepper to taste.

5 Place casserole in the centre of the oven for about 30 minutes. Sprinkle with chopped parsley before serving.

Three meals a day
on 1500 Calories or 15 carbohydrate units

Most people prefer to eat three really good meals a day, rather than snacking at intervals. Provided you limit your daily intake of food to 1,500 Calories or 15 carbohydrate units you can happily continue to enjoy substantial meals and at the same time gradually reduce those unwanted bulges.

The dishes suggested in the menus look so tasty and generous that other people will not even guess you are dieting. They are nourishing and sustaining so you should not feel hungry between meals. You are allowed 275 ml [½ pt] milk for drinks and cereal, but no sugar—use artificial sweetener only.

Basic savoury soufflé omelette

If soufflé omelettes are new to you, you will find them lighter than the traditional French omelette.

Calories: 220
Carbohydrate units: 0

SERVES 1
2 medium-sized eggs
salt and pepper
10 ml [2 teaspoons] butter

1 Set the grill to its highest temperature. Separate the eggs into 2 bowls, making sure there is no trace of yolk in the whites.

2 Add 10 ml [2 teaspoons] water to the yolks and the seasonings to taste. Mix well with a fork.

3 Add a pinch of salt to the whites and beat until stiff enough to stand in soft peaks but not dry.

4 Pour the yolk mixture on to the whisked whites and fold in lightly but evenly with a metal spoon.

5 Put the butter in a small non-stick omelette pan and heat gently. Swirl the butter around the pan to coat the base and sides.

6 When the foam has subsided, pour in the egg mixture. Cook,

THREE MEALS A DAY ON 1,500 CALS OR 15 CU			
Low-Calorie	**Cals (CU)**	**Low-carbohydrate**	**CU (Cals)**
MEAL 1:		MEAL 1:	
25 g [1 oz] sugared breakfast cereal		175 ml [6 fl oz] fresh orange juice	
150 ml [¼ pt] skimmed milk		**Cheddar cheese**	
75 g [3 oz] grilled kipper	290 (6½)	**soufflé omelette**	3 (340)
MEAL 2:		MEAL 2:	
100 g [¼ lb] lean mince and 1 small onion		1 avocado pear filled with 50 g [2 oz] prawns, coated with blender mayonnaise (page 48) and garnished with 15 ml [1 tbs] flaked toasted almonds	
100 g [¼ lb] grated carrot with 10 ml [2 tsp] flaked almonds and **piquant buttermilk dressing**			
150 ml [¼ pt] yoghurt	475 (3½)	1 fresh plum	1½ (965)
MEAL 3:		MEAL 3:	
225 g [½ lb] melon		100 g [¼ lb] grilled lamb chop plus 60 ml [4 tbs] boiled rice, served with Indian curry sauce (page 34)	
Fluffy cauliflower cheese with raw mushrooms			
125 g [¼ lb] baked potato		100 g [¼ lb] broccoli	
1 baked tomato		Orange fruit jelly (page 56)	8 (470)
100 g [¼ lb] Brussels sprouts			
Grape sorbet (page 54)	550 (11½)		
EXTRA:		EXTRA:	
252 ml [½ pt] milk	185 (2½)	275 ml [½ pt] milk	2½ (185)
Total:	1,500 (24)		15 (1,960)

Recipes in bold are given in this chapter.

Frederick Mancini

without stirring, for about 90 seconds, or until the bottom is set. Then place the pan immediately under the hot grill about 5 cm [2″] beneath the heat. Cook for about 30 seconds until the top of the omelette is puffy and golden.

7 Remove from the heat and serve immediately.

Variations

● Add 15 ml [1 tablespoon] freshly chopped herbs to the egg yolks when adding the seasoning.
     Calories: 220
     Carbohydrate units: 0
● Scatter 15 g [$\frac{1}{2}$ oz] grated Edam or Cheddar cheese over the top of the omelette before placing under grill.
     Calories: with Edam—265; with Cheddar—280
     Carbohydrate units: 0
● Crumble one crisply grilled rasher of streaky bacon over the cooked omelette before serving.
     Calories: 270
     Carbohydrate units: 0

Basic buttermilk dressing

Traditional vinaigrette and dressings based on mayonnaise for cold meats, fish or salads are prohibitive to the low-Calorie slimmer because of the large proportion of oil used to make them. To the low-carbohydrate slimmer this is of no consequence. But for others a continuous diet which includes dry salads becomes unpalatable and the low-Calorie slimmer eventually gives in to some high-Calorie sauce. Instead of succumbing to temptation, try this basic buttermilk dressing.

Buttermilk provides an excellent base for creamy-tasting, yet low-Calorie dressings. This is the basic recipe; vary it in the ways suggested.

Calories: 15
Carbohydrate units:
     negligible

MAKES ENOUGH FOR 1
     SALAD
45 ml [3 tablespoons]
     buttermilk
salt
freshly ground black pepper
squeeze of lemon juice

1 Season the buttermilk to taste with salt and pepper. Add a good

squeeze of lemon juice and stir well to mix.

Variations

● For a piquant dressing to serve with fresh green salads and crunchy vegetable salads, or as a sauce with lightly boiled green vegetables, place 15 g [$\frac{1}{2}$ oz] blue cheese in a small bowl. Mash with a fork until smooth. Gradually blend in the buttermilk, seasonings and lemon juice, plus a good pinch of cayenne pepper.
     Calories: 70
     Carbohydrate units: negligible
● For a herb dressing, simply add 5 ml [1 teaspoon] freshly chopped herbs to the basic dressing.
     Calories: 15
     Carbohydrate units: negligible
● For a cooling mint dressing to serve with cucumber salad, add a little finely chopped garlic plus 5 ml [1 teaspoon] freshly chopped mint or chives to the basic dressing.
     Calories: 15
     Carbohydrate units: negligible
● Make a spicy sweet dressing for ham or citrus salads by adding 5 ml [1 teaspoon] each horseradish and apple purée to the basic dressing.
     Calories: 25
     Carbohydrate units: negligible
● For a pink vegetable salad dressing stir 2 finely chopped stuffed olives, 5 ml [1 teaspoon] tomato purée and a pinch of paprika into the basic dressing:
     Calories: approximately 30
     Carbohydrate units: negligible
● For a sweet sauce to serve with fresh fruit salads, omit the lemon juice and seasonings. Place 5 ml [1 teaspoon] marmalade in a small bowl and gradually blend in the buttermilk. Add a little grated orange zest and a squeeze of orange juice.
     Calories: 35
     Carbohydrate units: 2

Fluffy cauliflower cheese

More substantial than a soufflé and more interesting than a simple cauliflower cheese, this is a dish that all the family can enjoy. For a satisfying meal, serve with baked tomatoes and boiled potatoes, but remember a 100 g [$\frac{1}{4}$ lb] potato adds 100 Calories or 4 carbohydrate units!

Non-slimmers could have some triangles of crisp, fried bread and bacon as a garnish if liked.

**Slimmer's portion, depending
on the amount of cheese**

used, serving 4:
     Calories: 295-325
     Carbohydrate units: 2
Slimmer's portion, serving 6:
     Calories: 195-220
     Carbohydrate units: 2

SERVES 4–6
700 g [1$\frac{1}{2}$ lb] cauliflower florets
25 g [1 oz] butter or margarine
25 g [1 oz] flour
**50 g [2 oz] skimmed milk
     powder**
2 medium-sized eggs
**75-100 g [3-4 oz] strong
     Cheddar cheese, grated**
**2.5 ml [$\frac{1}{2}$ teaspoon] mustard
     powder**
salt
freshly ground black pepper

1 Heat the oven to 200°C [400°F] gas mark 6.

2 Blanch the cauliflower florets in boiling salted water in a large saucepan. Drain well, reserving 575 ml [1 pt] of the liquid.

3 To make the sauce, melt the fat in a large saucepan. Remove from the heat and stir in the flour. Return the pan to the heat and cook gently for a minute or two without browning.

4 Remove the pan from the heat and stir in skimmed milk powder. Next, gradually add the cauliflower liquid and stir until smooth.

5 Return to the heat and bring to the boil, stirring. Lower the heat, cover and simmer for 2 minutes. Then remove from heat.

6 Separate the egg into two bowls, then add the yolks to the sauce with the grated cheese and mustard. Add salt and pepper to taste.

7 Whisk the egg whites, with a pinch of salt, until they will stand in soft peaks, then fold the sauce carefully into the egg whites using a metal spoon.

8 Pour half the sauce mixture into a 1.7 L [3 pt] ovenproof dish. Arrange the cauliflower on top, then pour over remaining sauce.

9 Bake in the centre of the oven for about 40 minutes, until risen and golden brown. Serve at once.

Three meals a day
1000 Calories or 10 carbohydrate units

Some slimmers find that after a period of time they become 'stuck' at a certain weight and seem quite unable to move from this plateau, as it is called.

A strict diet of only 1,000 Calories or 10 carbohydrate units per day can jolt the system and start the flab shifting again. It is also the quickest method to choose if you have only a little weight to lose and want to lose it fast.

In either case, however, reducing your Calorie or carbohydrate unit consumption to such a 'slim' level is a fairly drastic course and should be followed for a maximum of two weeks only. Otherwise your general health could suffer. It also requires a considerable degree of willpower and is extremely difficult to sustain for longer than a short length of time.

The menus given in this section have been carefully chosen to provide three appetizing and filling meals which meet all the basic dietary requirements for the day. You are allowed 275 ml [½ pt] milk, but you must sweeten drinks with artificial sweetener (if necessary) and not with sugar.

Basic egg sauce

This basic sauce is not thickened by flour nor is it made with whole milk which makes it more suitable for slimmers than a roux. The Calorie and carbohydrate content is given for the full recipe. When calculating the count per portion, simply divide by the number of servings.

Calories: 130
Carbohydrate units: 1½

MAKES ABOUT 150 ML [¼ PT]
1 medium-sized egg
150 ml [¼ pt] skimmed milk
salt
freshly ground black pepper

1 Break the egg into a bowl and stir lightly with a fork to mix the yolk with the white.

2 Half fill a saucepan with water and bring to simmering point. Meanwhile, put the milk in a separate

---

THREE MEALS A DAY ON 1,000 CALS OR 10 CU			
Low-Calorie	**Cals (CU)**	**Low-carbohydrate**	**CU (Cals)**
MEAL 1: Half a grapefruit **Ramekin egg with ham** 1 tomato, grilled 1 small slice of wholemeal toast, thinly buttered	250 (3)	MEAL 1: Half a grapefruit **2 ramekin eggs** (one with ham, one with mushrooms) 1 crumpet, buttered	3 (315)
MEAL 2: **Lentil and vegetable potage with bacon** 1 dessert apple	330 (9)	MEAL 2: Salami salad: chop 6 asparagus spears and ½ a green pepper, mix, arrange on a bed of watercress and top with 50 g [2 oz] cream cheese mixed with 25 g [1 oz] chopped salami	0 (455)
MEAL 3: 150 g [5 oz] steamed or baked cod fillet with **basic tomato sauce sauce** 150 g [5 oz] green beans 50 g [2 oz] fresh pineapple topped with 15 g [½ oz] dates	235 (6)	MEAL 3: 350 g [¾ lb] baked or grilled lemon sole **150 ml [¼ pt] seafood sauce** 225 g [½ lb] cooked spinach Swiss pears (page 45)	4½ (600)
EXTRA: 275 ml [½ pt] milk	185 (2½)	EXTRA: 275 ml [½ pt] milk	2½ (185)
Total:	1,000 (20½)		10 (1,555)

Recipes in bold are given in this chapter.

Frederick Mancini

pan, and bring almost to the boil, then pour on to the egg.

3 Place the bowl over the pan of barely simmering water. The bowl should sit securely on the saucepan rim without the bottom of the bowl touching the water. Cook the sauce for about 10 minutes, or until thickened, stirring constantly. Season to taste. Take care not to overheat or the sauce will curdle.

4 Remove from heat and flavour as required.

Variations

● For cheese sauce, stir in 25 g [1 oz] grated mature Cheddar cheese. Add a pinch of mustard powder and season to taste with salt and pepper.
    Calories: 250
    Carbohydrate units: $1\frac{1}{2}$
● For caper sauce to serve with fish, stir in 10 ml [2 teaspoons] capers, a good pinch of paprika and salt and pepper to taste.
    Calories: approximately 130
    Carbohydrate units: $1\frac{1}{2}$
● For parsley sauce, stir in 15 ml [1 tablespoon] freshly chopped parsley and salt and pepper to taste.
    Calories: 130
    Carbohydrate units: $1\frac{1}{2}$
● For seafood sauce, stir in a few drops of anchovy essence and 15 g [$\frac{1}{2}$ oz] peeled prawns or shrimps. Season lightly with salt and pepper.
    Calories: 145
    Carbohydrate units: $1\frac{1}{2}$
● For a custard sauce to serve with stewed fruit and other puddings, omit the salt and pepper. To flavour the sauce, either infuse a vanilla pod when scalding the milk, or stir in a few drops of vanilla extract after the custard has thickened. In addition, any of the following may be added: a grating of nutmeg, a pinch of ground cinnamon, mixed spice or ginger, or a little grated orange or lemon zest.
    Calories: 130
    Carbohydrate units: $1\frac{1}{2}$

Lentil and vegetable potage

Strictly for those following a low-Calorie diet, this soup makes a warm and inviting lunch on a chilly day and is filling and very nourishing. The high carbohydrate content of the lentils and potatoes, however, precludes it from the low-carbohydrate diet. Serve the other portions to the

non-slimmers as a starter to their evening meal.

    Slimmer's portion, serving 4:
        Calories: 290
        Without bacon: 195
        Carbohydrate units:
        With or without bacon: 7
    Slimmer's portion, serving 6:
        Calories: 195
        Without bacon: 130
        Carbohydrate units:
        With or without bacon: 5

SERVES 4–6
175 g [6 oz] split red lentils
1 medium-sized onion
175 g [6 oz] potatoes
175 g [6 oz] leeks
1.1 L [2 pt] stock
salt and pepper
8 rashers streaky bacon (optional)

1 Peel and chop the onions and potatoes; wash and slice the leeks. Put the lentils into a sieve and wash under cold running water.

2 Put the vegetables, lentils and stock in a large saucepan. Stir well and bring to the boil. Then reduce the heat, half cover the pan and simmer for 30–40 minutes until vegetables and lentils are tender. Remove from heat.

3 Liquidize the soup in a blender or pass through a fine vegetable mill. Season carefully. Return the soup to the pan and reheat.

4 Meanwhile, grill the streaky bacon (if used) until crisp, then drain on kitchen paper. Pour the soup into individual dishes and crumble two bacon rashers over each serving.

Basic tomato sauce

Sauces and gravies quickly pile on the Calories and so are usually avoided by serious slimmers on a low-Calorie diet. However, this tomato sauce contains neither flour nor fat and is low in Calories.

    Slimmer's portion, 125 ml [4 fl oz]:
        Calories: 25
        Carbohydrate units: 2

MAKES APPROXIMATELY
    425 ML [$\frac{3}{4}$ PT]

225 g [$\frac{1}{2}$ lb] canned tomatoes
1 large onion
2.5 ml [$\frac{1}{2}$ teaspoon] dried basil
15 ml [1 tablespoon] tomato purée
salt and pepper

1 Peel the onion, then chop it finely.

2 Put the chopped onion and 150 ml [$\frac{1}{4}$ pt] water into a small saucepan together with the basil. Bring to the boil then reduce heat and simmer for about 7 minutes, until onion is just tender. Remove from the heat.

3 Add the tomatoes and tomato purée to the onion mixture, then put into the liquidizer and blend.

4 Return to the pan, season to taste and reheat.

Ramekin egg with tomato

This recipe provides a light meal that you can eat any time of day.

Calories: 90
Carbohydrate units: $\frac{1}{2}$

SERVES 1
1 medium-sized egg
1 medium-sized tomato
salt and pepper

1 Skin, de-seed, then chop the tomato. Put it in the bottom of a ramekin dish and season to taste.

2 Break the egg on top of the tomato.

3 Stand the ramekin on a trivet in a pan and then pour sufficient boiling water into the pan to come to within 12 mm [$\frac{1}{2}$"] of the top of the ramekin.

4 Cover the pan and simmer for 10–15 minutes until set.

Variations

● For a ramekin egg with ham, use 25 g [1 oz] lean chopped ham in place of the tomato.
    Calories: 140
    Carbohydrate units: 0
● For a ramekin egg with mushrooms, substitute 25 g [1 oz] finely chopped button mushrooms for the tomato. Beat mushrooms with egg and cook for 10–12 minutes.
    Calories: 85
    Carbohydrate units: negligible

SLIMMING SINGLES

When you are slimming on your own one of the greatest dangers is the 'I can't be bothered to cook' syndrome. With the right approach cooking for one can be creative and fun. Whether the other members of the family are out to lunch or supper or whether you are living on your own, here are nourishing simple-to-cook recipes for the single slimmer. A special section is devoted to packed lunches to take to the office.

Home on your own

Slimming when you are on your own and the family are all out should require only willpower and self discipline. After all, no one else is at home whose eating habits you need to take into account. You can set about planning—just for yourself—meals which are nourishing and as easy (if you are a busy mother) or as difficult (if you really enjoy cooking) as you care to prepare.

Organize yourself to know all the nutritious low-Calorie or low-carbohydrate foods. Plan a week in advance and shop for yourself accordingly. Take the strain out of slimming—help yourself to avoid eating the fattening snacks by not buying them in the first place. You cannot be tempted to eat something which isn't in the house.

Beansprouts bolognese is a quick yet nourishing meal for one person.

Prepare and cook as much as possible ahead of time so a proper meal is ready to eat when you are hungry. You will then be well fortified against feeling the need to nibble between meals. Then you can look forward to joining the others in the evening with a slimmer's portion of the family supper.

When the children come home from school, they often feel hungry and cannot wait until supper. Have fresh fruit available and cubes of cheese already cut up in the refrigerator. Teach them to help themselves to these and a glass of milk. This way you will not be tempted to join them in a mid-meal of sandwiches, cakes or biscuits. At the same time you will be encouraging good eating habits from childhood.

If you have a lot of bad eating habits to break and find it difficult to stop eating between meals, then having an additional incentive is very helpful. You will be less inclined to cheat if you:
● seek a friend or neighbour who is also trying to lose weight so you can compare your progress
● keep yourself very busy looking after the house and children
● pursue a hobby at home, such as gardening, sewing or flower arranging
● join a committee or a local slimming club

If you find yourself alone for supper, the recipes in this section will do very nicely.

David Levin

Chicken in asparagus sauce

A purée of canned asparagus provides the thickening for this sauce, avoiding the need for flour or cornflour. The chicken and asparagus flavours complement each other well, resulting in a tasty main dish.

Calories: 275
Carbohydrate units: 1½

SERVES 1
100 g [¼ lb] cooked chicken
1 celery stick
50 g [2 oz] button mushrooms
290 g [10½ oz] canned
asparagus spears
150 ml [¼ pt] skimmed milk
2.5 ml [½ teaspoon] dried
rosemary
salt
freshly ground black pepper
snipped chives to garnish

Cut the chicken meat into bite-sized pieces. Next, scrub and chop the celery, then wipe and slice the mushrooms.

Drain the asparagus spears and purée them in an electric blender, then put the resulting purée into a pan.

Stir in the skimmed milk, prepared vegetables and chicken. Add the rosemary and seasonings to taste.

Bring to the boil then lower the heat, cover and simmer for 20 minutes, stirring occasionally. Check the seasonings and garnish with snipped chives before serving.

Watercress eggs

Light, yet sustaining, this dish is a marvellous combination of flavours and textures. It is high in food value but low in Calories and the carbohydrate content is nil—a bonus for all slimmers.

Poaching eggs is a fairly simple operation, but if you feel nervous, then poach the eggs one at a time.

Calories: 230
Carbohydrate units: 0

SERVES 1
2 bunches of watercress
15 g [½ oz] Cheddar cheese

a squeeze of lemon juice
salt and pepper
a few drops of vinegar
2 medium-sized eggs

1 Wash and trim the watercress, discarding any hard stalks and yellow leaves. Grate the cheese.

2 Blanch the watercress in boiling water for 1 minute. Drain, then purée in a blender with the lemon juice. Season well, then spread over the bottom of an ovenproof serving dish and keep warm.

3 Heat 5–7.5 cm [2–3"] of water in a wide, shallow pan and add a few drops of vinegar. Break the eggs into separate saucers.

4 When the water is simmering, stir it round quickly with a spoon to make a whirlpool. Then slip in the eggs.

5 As soon as the water becomes still, roll each egg over with a perforated spoon so the whites enclose the yolks.

6 Poach the eggs for 3½–4 minutes, then lift out of the water with a perforated spoon and drain on kitchen paper.

7 Heat the grill to high.

8 Place the eggs on top of the watercress purée, then sprinkle grated cheese over each egg. Place under the hot grill to melt and lightly brown the cheese.

Variations
●For eggs Florentine, substitute 225–350 g [½–¾ lb] well washed spinach for watercress. Cook the spinach, drain and press it between two plates to extract as much liquid as possible. Separate the leaves by lifting with a fork to lay in the base of an ovenproof dish and sprinkle over a little grated nutmeg. Keep warm and proceed as steps 3–8 above.
Calories: 350
Carbohydrate units: 0
●For egg soup, poach one medium-sized egg, by the method described, in 275 ml [½ pt] of liquid such as tomato juice or chicken or beef broth with 15 ml [1 tablespoon] of vermicelli. A little finely chopped celery, grated carrot or finely sliced onion can also be added for a quick light

meal. The eggs will need poaching a little longer than in water, about 6–7 minutes. Season and sprinkle with chopped parsley before serving.
Calories: 145
Carbohydrate units: in tomato—4; in broth—1½

Beansprouts bolognese

By substituting beansprouts for spaghetti you can avoid all the extra Calories and carbohydrates contained in the pasta, and still enjoy the sauce.

Calories: 255
Carbohydrate units: 1

SERVES 1
75 g [3 oz] minced beef
1 celery stick
1 garlic clove
salt
200 g [7 oz] canned tomatoes
2.5 ml [½ teaspoon] dried
marjoram
15 ml [1 tablespoon] dried
onion flakes
freshly ground black pepper
1 bay leaf
100 g [¼ lb] fresh or canned
beansprouts (drained
weight)

1 Scrub and chop the celery. Peel the garlic and crush on a plate with a little salt using a round-bladed knife.

2 Put the mince in a saucepan and place over a low heat. Breaking up the meat with a fork, allow the mince to brown in its own fat. Drain off the excess fat.

3 Pour the contents of the can of tomatoes over the mince in the saucepan. Add the chopped celery, crushed garlic, marjoram and dried onion flakes. Season well and add a bay leaf.

4 Stir the ingredients well with a wooden spoon and bring to the boil. Lower the heat and simmer gently for about 20 minutes.

5 Turn the beansprouts into a separate saucepan. Heat for 5 minutes, then drain and spread over the base of a serving dish.

6 Spoon the bolognese sauce over the beansprouts and serve.

Liver with orange

As liver has a fairly rich flavour, the orange provides a subtle freshness which makes this dish into a special one. For a vegetable, either spinach or spring greens would go well with it— 150 g [5 oz] of either only adds 20 Calories or negligible carbohydrate units to this main dish.

Calories: 350
Carbohydrate units: 2

SERVES 1
125 g [¼ lb] lambs' liver
1 orange
1 garlic clove
salt
15 g [½ oz] butter
90 ml [6 tablespoons] stock
1.5 ml [¼ teaspoon] dried
rosemary
freshly ground black pepper
chopped parsley to garnish

1 Wash the liver under running water, pat dry with kitchen paper, then trim and slice. Peel and segment the orange. Peel, then crush the garlic with a little salt.

2 Melt the butter in a frying-pan over medium heat. When the foaming ceases, add the liver and fry for 3 minutes on each side.

3 Drain off the excess fat. Pour over the stock, add the herbs and garlic and season well with salt and pepper.

4 Add the orange segments to the pan, cover and reduce the heat to low. Heat through for 1 minute.

5 To serve, turn the liver on to a warmed plate, then garnish with the parsley.

Lemony white cabbage

A very refreshing way to serve cabbage, especially as a bed for sage and onion mince (see below).

Calories: 20
Carbohydrate units:
negligible

SERVES 1
100 g [¼ lb] white cabbage
juice of half a lemon
salt

freshly ground black pepper
pinch of nutmeg

1 Remove any tough outer leaves and the thick stalk of the cabbage. Slice the rest of the cabbage thinly.

2 Bring 150 ml [¼ pt] water to the boil and add the cabbage. Cover, reduce the heat and simmer for 8 minutes until tender but still crisp.

3 Drain the cabbage. Stir in the lemon juice. Season with salt, pepper and a pinch of nutmeg to taste. Serve immediately.

Sage and onion mince

This slimmer's mince dish is a long way from shepherd's pie and beefburgers but just as tasty! Serve on a bed of lemony white cabbage for a filling meal.

Calories: 265
Carbohydrate units: 3

SERVES 1
100 g [¼ lb] lean minced beef
1 small onion
50 g [2 oz] carrots, trimmed
and scrubbed
2 tomatoes
5 ml [1 teaspoon] tomato
purée
15 ml [1 tablespoon] dried sage
salt
freshly ground black pepper

1 Peel and finely slice the onion. Grate the carrots. Skin and roughly chop the tomatoes.

2 Put the mince over a low heat in a non-stick saucepan. Breaking up the meat with a wooden spatula, brown evenly. Pour off any liquid fat.

3 Stir in the tomato purée and dried sage. Add the grated carrots and the onion together with 90 ml [6 tablespoons] water. Bring to the boil. Lower the heat, cover and simmer 15 minutes, stirring occasionally.

4 Remove the pan from the heat. Add the tomatoes and return to simmer a further 10 minutes. Season to taste with salt and pepper.

Cider chicken and sweetcorn

Chicken, lower in Calories than other meats, is a slimmer's blessing and here is just one way to treat it. Serve it on a bed of beansprouts (125 g [¼ lb]) or 25 g [1 oz] brown rice cooked in the normal way and you will satisfy your palate and purse.

Calories:
With rice: 335
With beansprouts: 305
Carbohydrate units:
With rice: 10½
With beansprouts: 5½

SERVES 1
100 g [¼ lb] boned chicken
breast, skinned
1 small onion
50 g [2 oz] green pepper
25 g [1 oz] canned or frozen
sweetcorn
150 ml [¼ pt] dry cider
salt
freshly ground black pepper

1 Peel and slice the onion. De-seed and slice the pepper.

2 Place the chicken in small pan and brown quickly over medium heat on both sides.

3 Add the onion and green pepper with the sweetcorn. Stir in the cider and season well. Bring to the boil and then lower the heat, cover and simmer gently for 15 minutes stirring occasionally, until the chicken is cooked right through the centre.

Egg mayonnaise

The large proportion of oil in conventional mayonnaise may be all right for those following a low-carbohydrate diet, but it is disastrous for low-Calorie slimmers. Here is a yoghurt version which is pleasantly flavoured, has a creamy texture and is low in Calories. The flavour is greatly improved if the mayonnaise is made in advance so that the seasoning is allowed to blend with the yoghurt. Combined with hard-boiled eggs and salad it makes a light, yet nourishing lunch.

Calories:
The salad: 185
The mayonnaise: 95

An appetizing meal for the single slimmer—cider chicken and sweetcorn.

Mock pizza

Quick to make, this is a spicy snack for one of your busier days. Serve with a plain green salad.

Calories: 225
Carbohydrate units: 5½

SERVES 1
25 g [1 oz] mushrooms
25 g [1 oz] Edam cheese
1 anchovy fillet or 5 ml [1 teaspoon] anchovy essence
2 stuffed olives
1 large slice bread
15 ml [1 tablespoon] tomato ketchup
2.5 ml [½ teaspoon] Worcestershire sauce
pinch dried mixed herbs

1 Heat the grill. Wipe and chop the mushrooms. Grate the cheese. Drain the anchovy fillet (if using) on kitchen paper. Slice the olives.

2 Toast the bread on both sides under the grill. Remove and keep warm.

3 Put the mushrooms in a small non-stick pan with the ketchup, Worcestershire sauce and herbs. Cook gently over a low heat, stirring, until the mushrooms are tender, about 3 minutes.

4 Spread the mushroom mixture on the toast. Sprinkle the grated cheese over the mushroom mixture.

5 Cut the anchovy fillet in two lengthways and place on top of the cheese in the form of a cross, or dot the cheese with anchovy essence. Finally, top with the sliced olives.

6 Return the toast to the grill to melt the cheese. When it is bubbling and golden serve at once.

Variation
● To serve two, warm a pitta bread on both sides under a low grill. Cut off one long edge, discard and split the pocket into halves. Make double the quantity of mushroom pizza mixture and arrange on the pitta as described for toast above.
Calories: 190
Carbohydrate units: 3½

Roger Phillips

Set aside.

Carbohydrate units:
The salad: ½
The mayonnaise: ½

SERVES 1
For the salad:
half a small lettuce
2 medium-sized hard-boiled eggs
1 medium-sized tomato
2 spring onions
snipped chives

For the slimmers' mayonnaise:
125 ml [4 fl oz] low-fat natural yoghurt
2.5 ml [½ teaspoon] mustard powder
5 ml [1 teaspoon] cider vinegar
salt and pepper

1 To make the mayonnaise, put the yoghurt into a medium-sized bowl and add the mustard and vinegar.

Mix well together until smooth and creamy, then season to taste.

2 Next, wash and dry the lettuce and arrange the leaves on a plate. Slice the hard-boiled eggs and place them on top. Pour over the yoghurt mayonnaise.

3 Thinly slice the tomato. Trim and chop the spring onions. Arrange the tomato and spring onions round edge of the egg mixture; sprinkle over the snipped chives.

Variation
● Instead of using plain mayonnaise for this dish, try slimmers' green mayonnaise. To make this, simply stir in 2 sprigs of freshly chopped tarragon and 30 ml [2 tablespoons] freshly chopped parsley. Store in the refrigerator for a few hours before using. The Calories and carbohydrate units remain the same.

This mayonnaise is also excellent served with the cold trout dish given on page 47.

Star recipe

Savoury haddock

This thick, richly-flavoured stew makes an ample dish for one person. Follow with a piece of fresh fruit to complete the meal.

Calories: 290
Carbohydrate units: 6½

SERVES 1
100 g [¼ lb] fresh haddock fillet
25 g [1 oz] streaky bacon
1 medium-sized onion
50 g [2 oz] potato, peeled
225 g [½ lb] canned tomatoes
15 ml [1 tablespoon] lemon juice
salt and pepper
chopped parsley

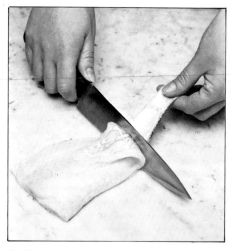

1 Remove the skin from the fish by easing it away from the flesh with a knife, then pulling gently with your fingers. Cut the flesh into cubes and put to one side.

2 Carefully remove all the rind from the streaky bacon, then chop the bacon into small pieces. Peel, then chop the onion and dice the potato. Set aside.

3 Put the bacon in a heavy-based pan over a medium heat. Cook gently, until the fat runs, then stir in the onion and potato. Sauté until the onion is soft.

4 Add the contents of the can of tomatoes, together with the lemon juice and bring to the boil. Then add the fish and season to taste with salt and pepper.

5 Reduce the heat and simmer, uncovered, for 20 minutes or until the fish flakes easily when tested with a fork. Check seasoning, garnish and serve.

Office lunches

One way to acquire unwanted Calories or carbohydrate units is to have snacks between meals. For instance, if you feel hungry before lunch you may be tempted to have a mid-morning snack. This may result in your not feeling like lunch but, instead of waiting to get home to a good supper, you stop for a nibble mid-afternoon. To combat this type of trap, eat a sound breakfast.

Then there's the question of what and where to eat for lunch when away from home. All too often the limited choice on a menu in a canteen or at the corner café includes stodgy pies, sausages and chips or sandwiches. If you must resort to eating lunch out, then try to choose a salad and follow with a yoghurt or a piece of fresh fruit. If you lunch at the local pub, the choice will be even more limited. Undoubtedly you will be persuaded to have a drink or two as well, which plays havoc with the slimmer's best intentions. On the occasional pub visit, choose low-Calorie mixers, tomato juice or a glass of dry white wine, and eat a sausage or a portion of cheese.

With all the limitations that eating out imposes on the slimmer, it is no wonder if you become bored, are tempted to eat fattening foods and then fail.

Your best plan would be to provide yourself with a different deliciously tempting packed lunch for each working day. In the fine weather you can take it to a nearby park and enjoy some sunshine as well.

If you have shopping to do in your lunch hour, then eat your packed lunch first, otherwise you may be tempted to buy and eat an unwanted chocolate bar. It really is very important to avoid the temptation of putting anything into your shopping basket which is not strictly part of your slimming plan.

Handy hints

Salt draws the liquid from some foods such as cottage cheese, tomato and cucumber, so it is a good idea to season your packed lunch just before eating, otherwise you may find your meal soggy and decidedly unappetizing.

To pack a lunch every day, you must be well organized, with the right food bought and ready to prepare the night before or first thing in the morning before you leave for work. The packed lunch ideas in this section can all be prepared quickly.

Useful equipment

Liquidizer: for making creamy soups, pâtés and cheese dips
Wide-necked flasks: to transport hot home-made soups on cold wintry days or refreshing fresh fruit and yoghurt salad in summer
Plastic containers: one large to keep salad vegetables crisp, two or three smaller ones for home-made pâtés, yoghurts and creamy cheese dips
Aluminium foil: to wrap cheese portions, cooked chicken joints and hard-boiled eggs
For the office drawer: set of cutlery, one small plate, refillable container for washing-up liquid, salt and pepper, mustard

Cheesy vegetable soup

There are times when even the most dedicated eater of packed lunches welcomes something hot and comforting. This vegetable soup is filling and tasty. Transport the soup in a wide-necked vacuum flask and pack the grated cheese separately to sprinkle over just before serving. The quantities given make enough for four servings. It will keep, covered, in the refrigerator for 3–4 days. When serving at home, stir the cheese into the soup. For a quick supper, sprinkle over each portion an extra 25 g [1 oz] grated Edam cheese and 15 ml [1 tablespoon] breadcrumbs. Place under a hot grill until golden and bubbling.

Slimmer's portion, 350 ml [12 fl oz]:
    Calories: 165
    Carbohydrate units: 1½
Slimmer's portion with extra cheese and breadcrumbs:
    Calories: 285
    Carbohydrate units: 2½

MAKES 1.4 L [2½ PT]
100 g [¼ lb] onions
100 g [¼ lb] leeks
100 g [¼ lb] celery
100 g [¼ lb] white cabbage
100 g [¼ lb] carrots
1 garlic clove
salt
15 ml [1 tablespoon] vegetable oil
850 ml [1½ pt] beef stock
freshly ground black pepper
5-10 ml [1-2 teaspoons] freshly chopped parsley

To serve:
100 g [¼ lb] Edam cheese

1 Peel, then slice the onions. Trim, shred and wash the leeks. Wash, then finely chop the celery and white cabbage. Scrub and trim the carrots, then chop into small pieces.

2 Peel the garlic, then crush with a little salt using a round-bladed knife.

3 Heat the oil gently in a medium-sized saucepan. Add the prepared vegetables and cook for 2–3 minutes, stirring constantly.

4 Stir in the garlic and stock and bring to the boil. Reduce the heat, cover and leave to simmer for about 25 minutes or until all the vegetables are tender.

5 Pare the red rind from the cheese, then grate the cheese. Reserve.

6 Season the soup with salt and pepper to taste and stir in the parsley. Serve the soup hot with 25 g [1 oz] grated cheese sprinkled over each serving.

Creamy mushroom soup

This thick creamy soup is delicious hot or chilled. The quantity given below provides enough for two servings. You can refrigerate half the soup in a container for up to two days.

Slimmer's portion:
    Calories: 115
    Carbohydrate units: ½

MAKES 2 SERVINGS
225 g [½ lb] button mushrooms
1 small onion
15 g [½ oz] butter
150 ml [¼ pt] skimmed milk
425 ml [¾ pt] chicken stock
salt
freshly ground black pepper

1 Peel, then chop the onion. Wipe, then chop the mushrooms.

2 Melt the butter in a saucepan and add the onions and mushrooms and sauté for 2 minutes. Pour in the milk and stock, then cover the pan and simmer for 20 minutes.

3 Remove from the heat and allow to cool slightly, then purée in an electric blender. Check seasoning. Return the soup to the pan and reheat until boiling.

Tuna and apple salad

A fish salad makes a welcome change from the usual cheese and ham salad. The vegetables provide a crunchy contrast to the soft texture of the fish. This is a very satisfying dish as the tuna fish contains a good supply of protein and minerals.

Calories: 460
Carbohydrate units: 3

SERVES 1
100 g [¼ lb] canned tuna fish
75 ml [3 fl oz] low-fat natural yoghurt
15 ml [1 tablespoon] lemon juice
salt
freshly ground black pepper
1 medium-sized tomato
1 celery stick
1 dessert apple
a few snipped chives
quarter of a lettuce

1 Drain the tuna thoroughly, discarding the oil. Turn the fish into a bowl and flake roughly with a fork.

2 Make the dressing by mixing the yoghurt and lemon juice together. Season to taste with salt and pepper then set on one side.

3 Roughly chop the tomato and add to the tuna fish. Scrub, then chop the celery and add to the fish. Core, then chop the apple and add together with the snipped chives.

4 Pour in the dressing and mix the ingredients gently together. Transfer to an airtight polythene container.

5 Wash and dry the lettuce and pack separately in a polythene bag.

6 To assemble the salad, season the tuna mixture with salt, then turn out on to a bed of the prepared lettuce leaves.

Sausage, apple and cabbage salad

Made with a red-skinned apple, this is a particularly colourful salad with an unusual flavour. The apple can be cored, if preferred. If you wish to transport it, put the salad in a sealed container.

Calories: 170
Carbohydrate units: 2½

SERVES 1
50 g [2 oz] well-grilled pork sausage
quarter of a small white cabbage
1 medium-sized dessert apple
1 celery stick
30 ml [2 tablespoons] cider vinegar
pinch mustard powder
dash soy sauce
few drops of liquid artificial sweetener (optional)
salt
freshly ground black pepper

1 Cut the cold sausage into bite-sized pieces and place in a bowl. Shred the cabbage finely and add to the bowl. Chop the apple and celery and add these. Mix all the ingredients in the bowl together.

2 To make the dressing, put the vinegar in a small bowl together with the mustard and soy sauce. Beat together and add sweetener if wished. Season to taste with salt and pepper.

3 Pour the dressing on to the salad. Chill and serve.

All-in-one salad

This salad can be made the evening before required and packed in an airtight container ready to take to work the next day. Keep the cheese separate and add it the following morning so it does not get too moist.

Calories: 365
Carbohydrate units: 5½

SERVES 1
1 large dessert apple
1 celery stick
half a medium-sized green pepper
50 g [2 oz] carrot, scrubbed and trimmed
15 g [½ oz] sultanas
30 ml [2 tablespoons] low-fat natural yoghurt
50 g [2 oz] Edam cheese
salt
freshly ground black pepper

1 Remove the apple core and chop the apple. Trim and chop the celery. De-seed the pepper, then slice. Grate the carrot coarsely. Wash, then dry the sultanas.

2 Put all the prepared fruit and vegetables into a bowl and stir in the yoghurt.

3 Pare the red rind from the cheese, then cut the cheese into cubes. Reserve.

4 Just before serving, add the cheese to the fruit and vegetable mixture. Season the salad with salt and pepper to taste.

David Levin

Slimming ploughman's lunch

A ploughman's lunch of bread, cheese and pickles may seem unsuitable for slimmers, but it need not be so. The ones normally served in pubs could cost you 800 Calories or 13 carbohydrate units. But—with just a few minor adjustments and a watchful eye on quantities—this delicious traditional meal makes an ideal packed lunch, which will not ruin your diet. Wrapped tightly in foil, the 'sandwich' is easy and convenient to transport. If the day's ration will allow, 275 ml [½ pt] of low-carbohydrate lager would add 80 Calories or 3½ carbohydrate units.

Calories: 350
Carbohydrate units: 6½

SERVES 1
50 g [2 oz] French bread
5 ml [1 teaspoon] French
 mustard
50 g [2 oz] Edam cheese
1 medium-sized tomato
1 spring onion, trimmed
2 pickled gherkins
salt
freshly ground black pepper

1 Slice the bread in half lengthways and pull out the doughy centre. Discard the centre and spread the cut sides with mustard.

2 Pare the red rind from the cheese, then cut the cheese into thin slices. Arrange the slices on one of the pieces of bread.

3 Thinly slice the tomato and gherkins, chop the onion and arrange on top of the cheese. Sprinkle with salt and pepper, then place the other piece of bread on top, pressing down firmly to hold the filling in place.

Slimming ploughman's lunch provides a hearty 'sandwich' at the office.

Crudités with spicy cottage cheese dip

This crunchy, vitamin-rich lunch can be prepared in the evening and refrigerated overnight.

Choose young, tender vegetables for the crudités. For variety, try sliced raw fennel, raw cauliflower florets, or cooked cold French beans in place of some of the vegetables suggested.

Calories:
The crudités: 70
The dip: 45
Carbohydrate units:
The crudités: 2
The dip: negligible

SERVES 1
For the crudités:
50 g [2 oz] carrot
50 g [2 oz] button mushrooms
50 g [2 oz] radishes
2 spring onions
half a medium-sized red or green pepper
2 celery sticks

For the dip:
100 g [¼ lb] cottage cheese

30 ml [2 tablespoons] low-fat natural yoghurt
5 ml [1 teaspoon] tomato ketchup
2.5 ml [½ teaspoon] curry paste
a pinch of chilli powder
salt
freshly ground black pepper

1 Scrub the carrot, then cut into thin strips like matchsticks; wipe and trim the mushrooms, radishes and spring onions. Remove any pith and seeds from the pepper, then cut into thin strips. Scrub and trim the celery, then cut into even-sized lengths. Pack the prepared crudités in an airtight plastic container.

2 Rub the cottage cheese through a sieve into a mixing bowl. Gradually mix in the yoghurt, beating well until the mixture is smooth and creamy. Beat in the tomato ketchup, curry paste and chilli powder, then season to taste with salt and pepper. Spoon the dip into another airtight plastic container.

Crudités with spicy cottage cheese dip—or as an alternative to the dip, try smoked mackerel pâté described on page 44.

Dip variations
To ring the changes, omit the tomato ketchup, curry paste and chilli powder and try any of these:
● For a garlicky dip, squeeze the juice from one garlic clove and beat into the dip with 5 ml [1 teaspoon] snipped chives. Spoon the dip into container and sprinkle with paprika.
Calories: 130
Carbohydrate units: negligible
● For a prawn dip, use cottage cheese with pineapple instead of plain cottage cheese. Do not sieve. Stir in 50 g [2 oz] roughly chopped prawns plus a pinch of cayenne after blending in the yoghurt.
Calories: 210
Carbohydrate units: ½
● For an anchovy dip, beat in 2.5 ml [½ teaspoon] anchovy essence, followed by 5 ml [1 teaspoon] each of capers and freshly chopped parsley. Season carefully.
Calories: 135
Carbohydrate units: negligible

Bedsitter suppers

At the end of a long day it is all too easy to push together a stodgy sandwich to eat with a cup of coffee, call that your supper, and then end up nibbling crisps or biscuits all evening to fill yourself up. Whether you need to watch your figure or not, this is not a particularly healthy eating pattern. Taking the trouble to organize a well-balanced supper will help you look better—and feel better too.

If you have no refrigerator and only two burners and a grill to cook on, the variety will be somewhat limited, but it is by no means impossible to prepare tempting meals for one which do not come out of a can.

Equip yourself with attractive crockery and glassware which will be a pleasure to use, making every mealtime an occasion to look forward to. Avoid enormous dinner plates. Choose instead a modest-sized plate that will comfortably accommodate single slimmer's portions. Oven-to-tableware is just as appropriate for use under the grill to warm a dish or to make a gratin ready to serve, and this saves on washing-up.

Buy fresh fruit and vegetables a little at a time and often, so that they are at their most nutritious. Remember, too, that they will be more tasty and less expensive when in season.

White fish, in particular, is excellent for slimmers, being high in protein, yet low in Calories. Eat fresh fish on the day of purchase.

Handy hints

Handy flavouring agents:
canned fish
canned pimento
canned tomatoes
curry powder or paste
dried herbs in small quantities
flavouring extracts
jar of stuffed olives
mustard
soy sauce
stock cubes
Tabasco sauce
wine or cider vinegar
Fresh herbs, such as parsley and mint, are well worth growing in pots on the windowsill—not only do they look attractive, but they also provide a fresh, aromatic garnish which will give a lift to the plainest of dishes.

Chicken casserole

This is a good example of a cold start casserole which has the advantage that there is no need to brown the meat in fat. Removing the skin from the chicken helps reduce the Calorie content of the dish.

Calories: 235
Carbohydrate units: 2

SERVES 1
175 g [6 oz] chicken joint
salt
freshly ground black pepper
1 medium-sized onion
1 small garlic clove
1 celery stick
50 g [2 oz] carrots
275 ml [½ pt] chicken stock
30 ml [2 tablespoons] white
    wine vinegar
bouquet garni
100 g [¼ lb] sliced frozen green
    beans

1 To remove the skin from the chicken, loosen the skin from the meat with the blade of a sharp knife and pull the skin away. Discard the skin.

2 Rinse the chicken joint, then pat dry. Sprinkle all surfaces with salt and pepper and rub in with your fingers.

3 Peel the onion and garlic, then slice finely. Scrub and trim the celery and carrots, then slice thinly.

4 Put the chicken joint in a heavy-based saucepan together with the sliced vegetables. Pour in the stock, then stir in the wine vinegar. Add the bouquet garni.

5 Cover the pan with a tight-fitting lid and bring slowly to simmering point. Simmer very gently for about 30 minutes. Add the green beans and simmer for a further 5–10 minutes or until the chicken is tender.

6 Using a slotted spoon, lift the chicken and vegetables on to a warmed serving plate and keep warm. Bring the liquid in the pan to the boil and boil until well reduced. Remove the bouquet garni, check seasoning and pour over the chicken and vegetables.

Piquant liver

Liver is low in Calories but high in protein, vitamins and iron. Cooked this way it is very tasty. For a complete meal, serve with 40 g [1½ oz] (raw weight) boiled brown rice.

Calories: 270
    With rice: 420
Carbohydrate units: 2
    With rice: 9½

SERVES 1
75 g [3 oz] lambs' liver
1 small onion
1 celery stick
50 g [2 oz] mushrooms
1 rasher streaky bacon
50 g [2 oz] carrot, scrubbed
    and sliced
15 ml [1 tablespoon] soy sauce
45 ml [3 tablespoons] natural
    low-fat yoghurt

1 Slice the liver into strips. Peel, then chop the onion. Scrub, then trim and slice the celery. Wipe, then slice the mushrooms. Set aside.

2 Chop the bacon, then fry gently in a non-stick pan until the fat runs. Add the liver and cook over a medium heat, stirring to seal all sides. Add the chopped onion, celery and carrot, lower the heat, then cook for a few minutes until softened.

3 Add the mushrooms. Stir in the soy sauce. Reduce the heat, cover and simmer gently for 10 minutes. Just before serving, stir in the yoghurt.

Ratatouille

This is a low-Calorie version of the famous French vegetable dish. The vegetables are cooked very gently until they almost disintegrate into the richly-flavoured sauce. Ratatouille is equally good hot or cold and makes a superb accompaniment to grilled fish and meat. Topped with grated cheese, it makes a marvellous main course in its own right—delicious with a mixed green salad.

The quantities given below provide enough for two helpings. So, if you are cooking for yourself, the second portion could provide your lunch the following day.

Slimmer's portion:
   Calories: 95
   Carbohydrate units: 3

MAKES ENOUGH FOR 2
SERVINGS
1 medium-sized aubergine
salt
1 medium-sized onion
1 small green pepper
2 medium-sized courgettes
225 g [½ lb] canned tomatoes
125 ml [4 fl oz] tomato juice
5 stuffed olives
1-2 garlic cloves
1 small bay leaf
2.5 ml [½ teaspoon] dried basil
freshly ground black pepper
freshly chopped parsley

1 Slice the aubergine, then sprinkle with salt and leave in a colander with a plate on top for about 30 minutes to draw out the bitter juices. In the meantime, peel and finely slice the onion; core, de-seed and chop the pepper; thickly slice the courgettes.

2 Rinse, drain, then pat the aubergine slices dry on kitchen paper. Put into a heavy-based saucepan together with the prepared vegetables.

3 Roughly chop the tomatoes and add to the pan, together with the juice from the can and the tomato juice. Chop the stuffed olives and add to the pan.

4 Peel, then finely chop the garlic and add to the pan, together with the bay leaf and basil. Mix the ingredients together and season to taste with salt and pepper.

5 Bring slowly to simmering point and cover with a tightly-fitting lid. Simmer gently, stirring occasionally, for about 45 minutes or until the vegetables are very tender. Remove the bay leaf and serve hot or cold, sprinkled with parsley.

Broccoli supper dish

Broccoli has a beautifully firm consistency even when well cooked; here it is served with a protein-rich sauce.

Calories: 365
Carbohydrate units: 1½

SERVES 1
225 g [½ lb] broccoli spears
150 ml [¼ pt] cheese sauce (see page 13)
15 g [½ oz] Cheddar cheese, grated
75 g [3 oz] canned pimento, drained

1 Trim the broccoli, then cook in barely simmering water for 8–10 minutes or until just tender.

2 In the meantime, prepare the cheese sauce as directed on page 13.

3 Heat the grill to moderate. Drain the broccoli thoroughly and place in a shallow, flameproof dish. Pour over the cheese sauce, then scatter over the grated cheese.

4 Cut the pimento into strips and arrange lattice fashion over the top. Place under the grill until the cheese has just melted and the pimento is heated through.

Globe artichoke with salmon dressing

This luxurious party hors d'oeuvre will make an imaginative supper for one person. Not only is it interesting to eat, but it is also very filling—bonus points for the slimmer.

Calories:
With soured cream: 230
With buttermilk: 210
Carbohydrate units: negligible

SERVES 1
1 large globe artichoke
a wedge of lemon
90 g [3½ oz] canned pink salmon
3 stuffed olives
1 spring onion
freshly chopped parsley
salt

Globe artichoke with salmon dressing makes a superb slimmer's supper.

Frederick Mancini

freshly ground black pepper
pinch grated nutmeg or mace
25 ml [5 teaspoons] soured
cream or buttermilk

1 Cut the stalk off the artichoke and remove any tough outer leaves. Thoroughly rinse the artichoke, shake dry, then rub the cut parts with lemon. Next, trim the tips of the leaves.

2 Bring a saucepan of salted water to the boil. Add a squeeze of lemon juice. Plunge the artichoke upside down into the water and cook for 30–40 minutes or until the leaves will pull away easily.

3 In the meantime, prepare the stuffing. Drain the oil from the salmon, then turn the fish into a bowl. Mash thoroughly with a fork. Finely chop the olives and add to the fish. Trim and finely chop the spring onion and add to the fish, together with the parsley, seasonings and spice.

4 Mix the ingredients together, then blend in the soured cream or buttermilk.

5 Drain the cooked artichoke, wrap in kitchen paper and squeeze gently to extract water. Stand upside down and leave until cool enough to handle.

6 Stand the cooled artichoke right-side up and gently ease open. Pull out the small inner purplish leaves —they should come out quite easily together with the hairy choke. Using a teaspoon, scrape out any remaining choke and discard.

7 Carefully spoon in the salmon mixture. Leave the artichoke until quite cold.

8 To eat, pull off a leaf, dip in the stuffing and scrape off the fleshy base of the leaf between your teeth. Discard the rest of the leaf. When all the other leaves are eaten, cut the artichoke base into chunks and eat with any remaining stuffing.

Variation
● When fresh artichokes are unavailable, use two drained canned artichoke hearts instead. Cut into

quarters and arrange around the edge of a small serving plate. Sprinkle with lemon juice. Spoon the salmon mixture into the centre of the plate and dust with paprika. The Calorie and carbohydrate content are unchanged.

Cod with curry topping

Plainly grilled cod can be rather dry. A spicy coating makes this firm fish more interesting. If you are unable to obtain buttermilk, yoghurt may be substituted.

Calories: 205
Carbohydrate units: negligible

SERVES 1
175 g [6 oz] cod fillet
50 g [2 oz] cottage cheese
curry paste or curry powder,
 to taste
salt
freshly ground black pepper
5 ml [1 teaspoon] buttermilk
lemon juice
paprika
little flavourless oil for
 greasing

1 Sieve the cottage cheese into a small mixing bowl. Using a metal spoon stir in the curry paste or powder to taste. Season. Add the buttermilk and blend well with a fork.

2 Rinse the cod fillet under cold water, then pat dry with kitchen paper.

3 Heat the grill to high and brush the grid lightly with flavourless oil to prevent the fish sticking. Place the fish, skin-side up, on the grid and grill for 2–3 minutes to crisp the skin.

4 Remove from the grill and reduce the heat to moderate. Turn the fish over with a fish slice and sprinkle the surface with lemon juice.

5 Spread the curried mixture evenly over the surface of the fish, then dust with paprika. Return to the grill for about 8–10 minutes until the topping is golden and bubbling and the fish is opaque and flakes easily when tested with a fork.

Leek and ham gratiné

Depending on what is in season, this recipe can also be made with courgettes, mushrooms or broccoli, saving 30 Calories or 3 carbohydrate units. Celery can also be used instead of leeks, saving 45 Calories or 3 carbohydrate units.

Calories: 265
Carbohydrate units: 5

SERVES 1
175 g [6 oz] leeks
25 g [1 oz] lean ham
5 ml [1 teaspoon] cornflour
30 ml [2 tablespoons] skimmed
 milk powder
salt
freshly ground black pepper
pinch dry mustard
15 g [½ oz] Edam cheese,
 grated
15 ml [1 tablespoon] chopped
 walnuts or 30 ml [2
 tablespoons] breadcrumbs

1 Wash and slice the leeks.

2 Put 150 ml [¼ pt] of water in a small saucepan and bring to the boil. Add the leeks and bring back to the boil. Lower the heat and simmer for 3–5 minutes until just tender. Meanwhile dice the ham.

3 Drain the leeks well, reserving the liquid, and place the leeks in a small ovenproof dish. Stir in the ham and keep in a warm place.

4 Blend the cornflour and the skimmed milk powder in a cup with a little of the liquid in which the leeks were cooked, season and stir in the dry mustard (more mustard can be added according to preference).

5 Heat the grill.

6 In a small pan heat the remaining leak liquor to almost boiling. Remove the pan from the heat. Stir in the cornflour and skimmed milk paste. Return the pan to the heat and boil for one minute.

7 Pour sauce over the leek and ham mixture. Sprinkle over the grated cheese then the walnuts or breadcrumbs. Place under the grill until the top is bubbling and golden brown.

FAMILY MEALS

Preparing a slimming meal for yourself is relatively simple—much more difficult is to prepare a balanced family meal incorporating dishes which allow ample for the slimmer to eat as well. This chapter covers many family situations.

The weekend roast

The Sunday joint, complete with all the trimmings, is the ideal family meal. Slimmers take heart—you can join with the rest of the family and eat roast meat, provided you are really strict about abstaining from the high Calorie or high carbohydrate extras. Roast potatoes, Yorkshire pudding, traditional bread stuffing and flour thickened gravy are all definitely forbidden. Instead, take a larger portion of the accompanying green vegetables or salad. To end the meal, serve all the family with one of the desserts on pages 30–31 or 54–57.

By choosing your joint carefully you can reduce its fattening effect.

In the chart you will find joints recommended for slimmers. Basically, chicken, turkey and offal are less fatty than beef, lamb and pork. Lean pork is lower in Calories than beef or lamb, provided you trim away all visible fat.

Help yourself, as a slimmer, by choosing a roasting method that will leave the joint less, rather than more, saturated with fat. Serve all the family with unthickened gravy and a slimming stuffing. They will not notice and it saves you from being tempted.

Always preheat the oven before roasting to prevent the meat from drying out.

Oven-roasting meat, uncovered: stand the joint on a grid or rack in the roasting pan, as this lets the fat drip away. This method also ensures that the meat will not fry in its own fat.

Oven-roasting meat covered: wrapped in foil or in a roasting bag the meat cooks without fat. Fat which escapes during cooking must be drawn off and the juices alone used for making gravy.

Spit-roasting meat produces succulent meat, with little fat, as this drips off during cooking. Awkwardly shaped joints, such as leg of lamb, are best boned and rolled to give an even shape.

Unthickened gravy for roasted meat: if you have a kitchen pipette or a baster, use this to draw off the fat from the roasting pan juices, otherwise pour off and then skim with a spoon. Add vegetable water to the juices in the normal way and also a dash of wine vinegar for added flavour. A little crushed garlic can be added, particularly when serving lamb. Boil vigorously, stirring up the sediment, until the liquid is reduced to 275 ml [½ pt]. Season and serve.

Slow-cooked pot roast: less fatty cuts, such as topside or poultry, can be cooked 6–8 hours or overnight at low setting—110°C [225°F] gas mark ¼—tightly covered in a thick casserole. Bed the joint on a layer of chopped vegetables such as carrots, onions and celery and add herbs and seasonings with 150 ml [¼ pt] of stock or wine. When cooked, transfer the meat and vegetables to a warmed serving dish. Skim the fat from the liquid left in the casserole, then boil the liquid to reduce by half. Pour into a sauce-boat and pass round.

Stuffings: avoid traditional stuffings with breadcrumbs or added fat. Choose vegetable stuffings or consider the type of stuffing which flavours the meat while cooking but is not eaten (e.g. mint leaves).

● For mint stuffing, wash then trim two good handfuls of mint sprigs. Salt and pepper the inside of a bird and put leaves in the cavity.

ROAST MEAT FOR SLIMMERS 100 g [¼ lb] lean cooked	Cals	CU
Bacon and Ham		
Back, collar, middle and corner gammon— smoked or unsmoked	480	0
Beef		
Sirloin for oven roasting	220	0
Topside and silver- side for pot roasting	180	0
Lamb		
Leg, loin and best end of neck (trim away all visible fat before cooking)	300	0
Pork		
Spare rib, blade, leg and loin	200	0
Poultry		
Chicken, off the bone, no skin	160	0
Turkey, off the bone, no skin	160	0
Duck, off the bone, no skin	220	0
Veal		
Loin, fillet and best end of neck	260	0

Stuffed boned and rolled roast is a family dish; serve with turnip, apple and raisin salad. Round off the meal with a frothy tangerine mousse.

● For cheese and onion stuffing, combine one chopped medium-sized onion with 225 g [½ lb] cottage cheese and season.
Calories: 220
Carbohydrate units: 2

Mixed vegetable stuffing for poultry

▨▨▨ *This quantity will stuff a 1.4 kg [3 lb] bird. The Calorie and carbohydrate units content are given for the complete stuffing but a 1.4 kg [3 lb] bird should serve 4–6 portions.*

Calories: 120
Carbohydrate units: 4

Giblets from one 1.4 kg [3 lb] chicken
bouquet garni
6 peppercorns
100 g [¼ lb] leeks
100 g [¼ lb] cooking apples
30 ml [2 tablespoons] chopped parsley
a large pinch of dried sage
salt
freshly ground black pepper

1 Wash the giblets, then put in a small saucepan with 150 ml [¼ pt] water, the bouquet garni and peppercorns. Bring to the boil, cover and simmer for 15 minutes.

2 Meanwhile, wash and finely chop the leeks, then peel and finely chop the apple. Put in a bowl.

3 Drain the giblets reserving the stock and the liver.

4 Finely chop the liver, then mix into the leeks and apple. Add the herbs. Season to taste and moisten with 30 ml [2 tablespoons] stock. (Keep the remaining stock for a thin soup.)

5 Loosen the skin away from the chicken breasts, then pack the stuffing under the skin and into the neck end of the bird.

Recipe for stuffing a boned and rolled roast

▨▨▨ *This quantity will stuff a 1.4 kg [3 lb] boned joint of veal, lamb or pork ready for rolling. The Calorie and carbohydrate contents are given for the whole stuffing but this amount should serve 4–6 portions.*

Calories: 50
Carbohydrate units: ½

½ small onion
100 g [¼ lb] cauliflower florets
salt
100 g [¼ lb] canned mushrooms
½ celery stick

15 ml [1 tablespoon] chopped parsley
2.5 ml [½ teaspoon] fresh thyme
fresh ground black pepper
5 ml [1 teaspoon] Worcestershire sauce

1 Peel and finely chop the onion. Wash cauliflower florets and cook until tender in boiling salted water. Drain and chop finely.

2 Drain and finely chop the mushrooms. Scrub and dice celery stick.

3 Combine the onion, cauliflower, mushrooms, celery, parsley and thyme together in a bowl. Season well and add Worcestershire sauce.

Variation

● For a tasty stuffing for pork, omit the celery and use a medium-sized apple instead. Peel, core and finely chop the apple before mixing with the other ingredients.
Calories: 135
Carbohydrate units: 3.

David Levin

The accompanying vegetables:
Low in Calories and carbohydrates, vegetables contain important vitamins and minerals that are essential for general good health. Purchase fresh vegetables frequently and in quantities which can be eaten within 2–3 days. They are best eaten raw, as none of the goodness is destroyed.

Cook vegetables in the minimum of water, tightly covered, over a high heat and for the minimum of time—a pressure cooker will do this admirably. Cooking in a steamer will have the same effect. Serve as soon as possible after draining; keeping vegetables warm destroys the vitamins in them.

Oven-braised celery hearts

Cooking celery in a little stock instead of boiling water gives the vegetable extra flavour. For a party, it turns a plain vegetable dish into something special. Tomato juice can be used instead of stock if preferred.

If the oven is heated for another dish, then it makes sense to use it for the celery. Otherwise you can braise the celery in a covered saucepan over a low heat on top of the stove. The cooking time will be about the same.

This braising method is also suitable for leeks, fennel, carrots, cucumber, onions, broccoli, marrow and endive.

Two tasty vegetable dishes: top, carrots with courgettes; below, fennel and oranges.

Slimmer's portion:
 Calories: 30
Carbohydrate units:
 negligible

SERVES 4
4 small or 2 large celery heads
150 ml [¼ pt] chicken stock
15 ml [1 tablespoon] lemon juice
salt and pepper

1 Heat the oven to 180°C [350°F] gas mark 4.

2 Remove the outer tough stalks from the celery, trim the stump then cut the celery down so each heart is 12.5–15 cm [5–6″] long. Slice large heads lengthways.

3 Put the celery hearts in a single layer in the bottom of a shallow ovenproof casserole.

4 Heat the stock until boiling, then pour over the celery hearts. Add the lemon juice and season to taste with salt and pepper.

5 Cover the casserole and bake towards the bottom of the oven for 1½ hours.

Turnip, apple and raisin salad

Nearly all root vegetables can be grated raw into salads. The turnips used in this salad combine well with the sharp apples and mustard; raisins add a sweet contrast. Serve this salad with grilled steak or cold roast beef.

Slimmer's portion of the salad:
Calories: 70
Carbohydrate units: 4½
Slimmer's portion of the dressing:
Calories: 35
Carbohydrate units: 0

SERVES 4
For the salad:
350 g [¾ lb] young, white turnips
225 g [½ lb] cooking apples
50 g [2 oz] raisins

For the dressing:
60 ml [4 tablespoons] soured cream
30 ml [2 tablespoons] white wine vinegar
15 ml [1 tablespoon] Dijon mustard
salt
freshly ground black pepper

1 Wash, trim and grate the turnips. Wash, core and finely chop the apples. Put the turnips and apples into a salad bowl with the raisins, and mix well together.

2 To make the dressing, beat the cream, vinegar and mustard together. Season and fold into the salad. Serve immediately.

Fennel and oranges

Florentine fennel and oranges make an impressive accompanying vegetable dish, especially for roast pork or chicken. This dish could also be served as a refreshing first course.

Slimmer's portion:
Calories: 130
Carbohydrate units: 1
Carbohydrate units: 1

SERVES 4
450 g [1 lb] Florentine fennel
1 garlic clove
45 ml [3 tablespoons] vegetable oil
salt
freshly ground black pepper
2 medium-sized oranges

1 Trim the fennel, discarding any tough outer stalk, then cut into slices about 12 mm [½″] thick. Peel and finely chop the garlic. Put the oil in a frying-pan over a low heat. Add the fennel and garlic. Season.

2 Cover the pan and cook gently for 15 minutes, turning the fennel occasionally.

3 Cut the rind and pith from the oranges. Cut the oranges into quarters lengthways and thinly slice across them. Turn the oranges into the pan with the fennel. Toss gently to mix, then cover again and cook for a further 2 minutes. Serve hot or cold.

Carrots with courgettes

This combination is better for the slimmer than traditional peas and carrots because peas have a high Calorie and carbohydrate content. By grating the carrot the two vegetables will cook together in the same pan for the same amount of time.

Slimmer's portion:
Calories: 15
Carbohydrate units: 1

SERVES 4
225 g [½ lb] carrots
225 g [½ lb] courgettes
5 ml [1 teaspoon] lemon juice
salt
freshly ground pepper

1 Scrub then grate the carrots.

Wash, then trim and slice the courgettes.

2 Put the vegetables in a saucepan with a little water. Bring the pan to the boil, cover and simmer for 7–10 minutes until the vegetables are just tender.

3 Drain the vegetables, return to the pan. Stir in the lemon juice, season with salt and pepper to taste. Stir over a low heat until piping hot and serve with chopped parsley sprinkled over if wished.

Red cabbage and carrot salad

This is a good, hearty, flavoursome winter salad. Serve with roast beef or lamb or as a light meal with cottage cheese.

Slimmer's portion of the salad:
Calories: 15
Carbohydrate units: ½
Slimmer's portion of the dressing:
Calories: 75
Carbohydrate units: negligible

SERVES 4
For the salad:
225 g [½ lb] red cabbage
100 g [¼ lb] carrots

For the dressing:
1 garlic clove
salt
60 ml [4 tablespoons] vegetable oil
30 ml [2 tablespoons] red wine vinegar
freshly ground black pepper
2 large pickled gherkins
5 ml [1 teaspoon] dill seeds

1 Trim and finely shred the cabbage. Scrub, then grate the carrots coarsely. Mix together in a salad bowl.

2 For the dressing, peel, then crush the garlic on a plate with a little salt, pressing it with a round-bladed knife.

3 Beat the oil, vinegar, garlic, salt and pepper together and pour over the salad. Finely chop the gherkins and toss with the dill seeds into the salad.

Tangerine mousse

▨▨ *This mousse is particularly delightful made with tangerines, but one orange may be substituted. Serve with sponge fingers to non-slimmers.*

Slimmer's portion:
Calories: 120
Carbohydrate units: 1

SERVES 4
2 tangerines
15 ml [1 tablespoon] gelatine
350 ml [12 fl oz] low-fat
tangerine or orange yoghurt
2 medium-sized egg whites

1 Grate the zest from the tangerines and reserve.

2 Put 30 ml [2 tablespoons] cold water into a heavy-based saucepan and sprinkle over the gelatine. Leave to soak for 5 minutes, then dissolve for 3 minutes over low heat without stirring. Remove from heat and allow to cool.

3 Turn the yoghurt into a large bowl and stir in the grated zest.

4 As soon as the gelatine has cooled, pour it into the yoghurt in a thin stream, stirring constantly. Leave in a cool place for about 30–45 minutes until just on the point of setting.

5 Put the egg whites in a spotlessly clean, dry bowl and whisk until stiff but not dry. Then gently fold into the mandarin mixture.

6 Divide the mixture between four glasses and chill in the refrigerator for about 30 minutes.

7 Remove all the white pith from the tangerines, then divide the flesh into segments. Serve the mousse decorated with segments.

Pear and walnut meringue

▨ *This is a quick and easy—but attractive—dessert which all the family will enjoy and it can be easily adapted to use other fruit. The combination of the cold fruit and hot meringue is deliciously refreshing, while the walnuts add texture.*

Slimmer's portion:
Calories: 100
Carbohydrate units: 2½

SERVES 4
2 ripe dessert pears
60 ml [4 tablespoons] chopped walnuts
2 medium-sized egg whites
25 g [1 oz] caster sugar

1 Heat the grill. Next, peel, halve and core the pears. Place the halves on an ovenproof plate, cut side up. Divide the chopped walnuts between the four pear hollows.

2 Whisk the egg whites until stiff, then fold in the sugar.

3 Spoon the whisked egg whites over the pear halves and place under the grill for 1–2 minutes to brown and crisp. Eat immediately.

Orange cheesecake

▨▨ *Although low in Calories, this is a beautiful cheesecake that a slimmer need have no hesitation in offering to visitors and family alike. Made without the fresh fruit topping, individual portions will keep well for 2–3 days, wrapped, in the refrigerator. For ease of serving whole, it is a good idea to use either a spring-form or a loose-bottom cake tin.*

Slimmer's portion:
Calories: 110
Carbohydrate units: 2
Without fruit topping:
Calories: 100
Carbohydrate units: 2

SERVES 8
2 large sweet oranges
3 digestive biscuits
350 g [¾ lb] cottage cheese
2 medium-sized eggs
40 g [1½ oz] caster sugar

1 Position shelf in centre of the oven, then heat the oven to 180°C [350°F] gas mark 4.

2 Grate the zest from one of the oranges and reserve.

3 Put the digestive biscuits in a strong polythene bag and tie a knot in the top. Reduce the biscuits to crumbs by rolling a rolling pin back and forth over the bag.

4 Sprinkle the crumbs evenly over the bottom of a 18 cm [7"] flan tin with a loose-bottomed base.

5 Put the grated orange zest, cottage cheese, eggs and sugar into a liquidizer and blend at high speed until smooth and creamy.

6 Pour the cottage cheese mixture into the flan tin and spread evenly over the biscuit crumbs.

7 Bake in the oven for about 45 minutes, until set. Remove the cooked cheesecake from the oven, allow to cool, then chill in the refrigerator.

8 To serve, carefully remove the cheesecake from the tin. Peel the oranges, cut the flesh into segments, removing any white skin, pith and pips, and decorate the top of the cheesecake with the orange segments.

Variations
● For orange and strawberry cheesecake, decorate the top of the cheese cake with 350 g [¾ lb] hulled fresh strawberries.
Calories: 110
Carbohydrate units: 2½
● For raspberry or blackberry cheesecake, omit oranges entirely and flavour the cheesecake with the zest of 1 lemon. Use 350 g [¾ lb] fresh raspberries or blackberries to decorate the top.
With raspberries:
Calories: 110
Carbohydrate units: 2½
With blackberries:
Calories: 115
Carbohydrate units: 2½

Strawberry ice-yoghurt

▨▨▨ *Although the texture of this slimmer's ice isn't quite the same as that of full dairy ice-cream, neither is the Calorie content and this version makes a refreshing dessert. Check that the container you use for freezing the ice-yoghurt will fit comfortably in the freezer compartment of the refrigerator. This dessert can be kept in the refrigerator and served the following day, if wished.*

Slimmer's portion:
Calories: 110
Carbohydrate units: ½

Alan Duns

SERVES 4
**3 medium-sized egg whites
350 ml [12 fl oz] low-fat
    strawberry yoghurt
12 fresh strawberries to
    decorate**

1 Turn the refrigerator to its coldest setting one hour before you start and chill either freezer trays or a shallow polythene container in which you will freeze the ice-yoghurt.

2 In a fairly large spotlessly clean, dry bowl, whisk the egg whites until fluffy and standing in soft peaks.

3 Gradually add the yoghurt to the egg whites, whisking all the time until all the yoghurt is thoroughly incorporated and the mixture is light and fluffy.

4 Spoon the mixture into the freezer trays or shallow polythene container. Cover with foil and put in the freezer compartment of the refrigerator for about 45 minutes until the mixture is solid around the edges.

An orange cheesecake to delight everyone.

5 Remove the container from the refrigerator. Using a fork, gently turn the frozen edges into the softer centre. Return the container to the freezer compartment for another hour or until the mixture is completely frozen.

6 To serve, put scoopfuls of the ice-yoghurt into four chilled glass serving bowls. Rinse and hull the fresh strawberries and place three on top of each portion.

Suppers and snacks

It is often when you need to make a meal in a hurry that good slimming resolutions fail, so you need a handful of resourceful ideas to fall back on.
● Fresh herbs lift plain vegetable dishes out of the ordinary. To ring the changes, try combining different textured vegetables.
● For very little extra outlay, a slightly larger weekly roast will provide the basis for at least one midweek supper and even a light lunch for the slimmer.
● Pulses are also useful for providing protein and are very filling.
● A small portion of protein added to a generous helping of vegetables makes a quick and nourishing snack.

If you, the cook of the household, are the slimmer then you will find it easier to resist the temptation of unwanted Calories and carbohydrate units if you do any food shopping or preparation after a meal.

Mixed vegetable chop suey

This tasty family supper is quick to cook, and can be made with other combinations of vegetables, according to the season. Serve with noodles.

Slimmer's portion with 50 g [2 oz] cooked noodles:
   Calories: 365
   Carbohydrate units: 3½

SERVES 4
350 g [¾ lb] onions
350 g [¾ lb] white cabbage
225 g [½ lb] button mushrooms
4 celery sticks
1 small red pepper
275 g [10 oz] beansprouts
10 ml [2 teaspoons] cornflour
10 ml [2 teaspoons] soy sauce
150 ml [¼ pt] chicken stock
6 medium-sized eggs
salt and pepper
45 ml [3 tablespoons] vegetable oil

1   Peel and chop the onions. Wash and shred the cabbage. Wipe and thinly slice the mushrooms. Scrub and chop the celery. De-seed and slice the pepper. Pick over the beansprouts, then rinse and drain.

2   In a small bowl, blend the cornflour, soy sauce and stock.

3   Break three eggs into another bowl. Add 10 ml [2 teaspoons] cold water and beat with salt and pepper to taste. Repeat with the other three eggs in a third bowl. Set both aside.

4   Heat 30 ml [2 tablespoons] of the oil over low heat in a large saucepan or wok. Add the onion and cook gently for 2 minutes without browning.

5   Add the cabbage, celery and pepper and cook for a further 2 minutes, stirring all the time. Add the mushrooms and beansprouts and cook for a further 60 seconds. Remove pan from the heat.

6   Stir the cornflour mixture then pour into the pan with the vegetables and stir well to mix. Return the pan to the heat. Bring to the boil and simmer 2 minutes or until the mixture thickens.

7   Season to taste. Reduce the heat, cover with a plate to keep the vegetables warm.

8   In a non-stick frying-pan, heat 7.5 ml [1½ teaspoons] of the remaining oil. Pour one bowl of eggs into the pan.

9   Cook the eggs for one minute to set the base of the omelette.

10 With a wooden spatula, pull the edges of the omelette towards the centre. At the same time, tip the pan away from you and from side to side to allow the raw egg to run to the pan sides.

11 As soon as all the egg is just on the point of setting, remove the pan from the heat. Tilt the pan away from you. Then, using a spatula, lift the edge of the omelette nearest you and fold towards the centre.

12 Tilt the pan a little further and flip the folded edge over, then roll the omelette out of the pan on to the plate covering the vegetables. (This will keep it warm.)

13 Make a second omelette in the same way, using the remaining beaten eggs. Slice both omelettes into thin strips and add these to the vegetables. Serve immediately.

Mushroom soufflé

With a little ingenuity a favourite recipe can often be adapted to make it equally suitable for the low-Calorie slimmer and family alike. In this recipe the amount of fat has been reduced; skimmed milk has been used and the mushrooms have been lightly simmered instead of fried. The result is as delicious as a traditional soufflé but with far fewer Calories.

   Slimmer's portion:
   Calories: 185
   Carbohydrate units: 3

SERVES 4
225 g [½ lb] button mushrooms
425 ml [¾ pt] skimmed milk
25 g [1 oz] butter or margarine
50 g [2 oz] flour
3 medium-sized egg yolks
salt
freshly ground black pepper
4 medium-sized egg whites
a little oil for greasing

1   Place a baking sheet in the centre of the oven and heat to 200°C [400°F] gas mark 6. Lightly grease a 2 L [3½ pt] straight-sided soufflé dish with oil.

2   Wipe, then finely chop the mushrooms.

3   Put the milk into a medium-sized saucepan over a medium heat and bring to the boil. Off the heat, add the mushrooms. Lower the heat and return the pan to simmer gently for 5 minutes. Set aside.

4   Melt the fat in a separate saucepan over a low heat and just as it froths add the flour. Mix well with a wooden spoon to make a roux. Off the heat, gradually pour in the milk and mushrooms, stirring all the time. Return to the heat, continue stirring and simmer for 2–3 minutes until thick.

5   Remove the saucepan from the heat and stir in the egg yolks. Season carefully with salt and pepper.

6   Add a pinch of salt to the egg whites and whisk until very stiff. With a metal spoon, stir one spoonful of egg white into the mushroom mixture, to loosen it, then fold in the remainder.

Star recipe

Slimmers' onion 'flan'

This is a flan with a difference. Instead of the usual pastry, spinach leaves are used to line the flan dish.

Slimmer's portion:
  Calories: 195
  Carbohydrate units: 2½

SERVES 4
25–30 fresh spinach leaves
salt
450 g [1 lb] onions
125 ml [4 fl oz] low-fat
  natural yoghurt
2 medium-sized eggs
100 g [¼ lb] Edam cheese
a pinch of mustard powder
freshly ground black pepper
1 large tomato, sliced

David Levin

1 Heat the oven to 200°C [400°F] gas mark 6. Bring a large pan of salted water to the boil. Meanwhile, wash the spinach leaves thoroughly, then trim the stalks level with leaves.

2 Using a sharp knife, remove any very coarse central stalks from the leaves. Blanch half the leaves for 2 minutes, then drain, separate and pat dry on kitchen paper. Repeat with remaining leaves.

3 Arrange the blanched spinach leaves in a 20 cm [8"] fluted china flan dish so that the bottom and sides of the dish are completely covered. Set the lined flan dish aside.

4 Peel, then chop the onions. Place chopped onions in a pan of boiling salted water and simmer for about 10 minutes, until just tender, then drain thoroughly.

5 Put the yoghurt in a small bowl. Add the eggs and beat until the mixture is smooth. Grate the cheese and stir into the yoghurt mixture together with the onions and mustard. Season well.

6 Pour the mixture into the spinach case. Top with slices of tomato, then bake in the centre of the oven for 30 minutes or until the filling has set. Serve hot or cold.

7 Carefully turn the soufflé mixture into the prepared dish and place in the centre of the oven on the baking sheet. Bake for about 45 minutes, until puffed up and browned on top. The soufflé should be served immediately.

French beans and bacon

Staying out of the kitchen as much as possible and away from the temptation to nibble is a great help to the slimmer, so this quick-to-prepare recipe is ideal.

The occasional use of frozen vegetables can save you time, as there is little or no preparation involved, but dress them up a little, or you will get bored with them. The open cooking with no liquid preserves a good crisp texture and the bacon gently flavours the beans and gives them an attractive appearance.

Slimmer's portion:
Calories: 50
Carbohydrate units:
negligible

SERVES 4
100 g [¼ lb] streaky bacon rashers
450 g [1 lb] frozen whole French beans
freshly ground black pepper

1 Trim the rind from the bacon and discard. Chop the bacon, place in a frying-pan and cook gently until the fat begins to run. Increase the heat and fry the bacon until it begins to brown. Drain excess fat.

2 Add the frozen beans and cook gently for about 5 minutes, stirring continuously, until the beans are heated through but still crisp and all the moisture in the pan has evaporated. Season with pepper.

Variety burgers

Brains, although reasonable in price, are considered a great delicacy. They are also low in Calories and very nutritious.

Some may not like the idea of handling brains in their raw state, but this delicious way of serving them makes any unpleasant preparation well worthwhile. Brains are very perishable and must be used immediately. Start pre-

parations as soon as possible after purchase.

Serve the burgers with broccoli spears and the caper sauce, or the tomato sauce on page 13.

Slimmer's portion:
Calories: 260
Carbohydrate units: 0

SERVES 4
450 g [1 lb] beef or calves' brains
1 large garlic clove
salt
5 ml [1 teaspoon] baking powder
a little paprika
4 medium-sized eggs
freshly ground black pepper
30 ml [2 tablespoons] vegetable oil

To garnish:
chopped parsley

1 Put the brains in a bowl and cover with cold water. Leave to soak for 1–2 hours, changing the water several times. This process whitens the brains.

2 Cut away any opaque bits at the base and peel away the thin membrane covering the brains. Leave to soak again until ready to use.

3 Peel and crush the garlic with the salt.

4 Drain the brains. Put half into a liquidizer with half of the garlic, 2.5 ml [½ teaspoon] baking powder and a little paprika. Add two of the eggs and blend together thoroughly. Pour into a clean mixing bowl.

5 Blend the rest of the brains in the same way and add to the mixture in the bowl. Mix well and season to taste.

6 Heat the oil in a non-stick frying-pan over a moderate heat. Fry large spoonfuls of the mixture in batches, so as not to overcrowd the pan, until golden brown on both sides.

7 Remove the cooked burgers from the pan with a wooden spatula, drain on kitchen paper and keep warm while frying the remainder. Garnish with parsley.

Winter salad

This is a very attractive salad which, with the protein of the kidney beans, makes a good supper dish. The combination of textures and flavours is also rather unusual.

Slimmer's portion:
Calories: 195
Carbohydrate units: 2½

SERVES 4
1 large curly endive
275 g [10 oz] canned red kidney beans
400 g [14 oz] canned artichoke hearts
15 ml [1 tablespoon] wine vinegar
a pinch of mustard powder
salt and pepper
60 ml [4 tablespoons] olive oil

1 Remove the centre core and tough outer leaves of the endive and discard. Separate the remaining leaves, wash, then dry.

2 Turn the kidney beans into a sieve and rinse under cold water. Pile in the centre of a salad bowl.

3 Drain the artichoke hearts and arrange these around the edge of the beans. Next, arrange the curly endive inside outer rim of bowl.

4 To make the dressing, put the vinegar in a small bowl. Add the mustard powder, salt and pepper. Using a fork, beat well to dissolve the mustard powder. Next, add the oil and beat again until well blended. Dribble over the artichoke hearts and kidney beans. Leave for at least two hours before serving, to allow the dressing to penetrate the vegetables.

Indian curry sauce

An authentic curry sauce is a very practical and tasty way to use up leftovers. Serve it with 100 g [¼ lb] chicken (160 Calories), 75 g [3 oz] lean roast beef (165) or lean roast lamb (225), 150 g [5 oz] white fish (150) or 1½ medium-sized hard-boiled eggs (120) – none have carbohydrate units. Serve on a bed of rice. Slimmers can help themselves to 60 ml [4 tablespoons] cooked rice (80 Calories or 4½ carbohydrate units).

Slimmer's portion of curry
sauce:
    Calories: 75
    Carbohydrate units: ½

SERVES 4
1 medium-sized onion
30 ml [2 tablespoons]
   vegetable oil
1 garlic clove, chopped
5 ml [1 teaspoon] turmeric
5 ml [1 teaspoon] ground
   cumin
2.5 ml [½ teaspoon] chilli
   powder
125 g [¼ lb] canned tomatoes
5 ml [1 teaspoon] salt
350 g [¾ lb] frozen peas

For non-slimmers:
450 g [1 lb] potatoes

1 Peel, then chop the onion. Heat
the oil in a medium-sized heavy-
based pan and add the onion and
cook gently for 5 minutes until soft
but not brown.

2 Add the garlic and spices and
stir over a gentle heat for 1 minute.

3 Add the tomatoes together with
the juice from the can. Then stir
in 275 ml [½ pt] water and the salt.
Increase the heat and bring to the
boil, then cover, reduce the heat
and simmer gently for 20 minutes.

A mushroom soufflé served with winter
salad provides a light family meal.

4 Meanwhile, for non-slimmers, peel
potatoes and cut into small
cubes. Put in a large saucepan,
cover with water, add salt and
bring to the boil. Cover and cook
10–12 minutes or until just tender.
Drain the potatoes and set aside.

5 Next, add the peas to the curry and
cook for 5–7 minutes, until the
peas are tender. Check seasoning.

6 Remove one portion for each slimmer to another pan and keep warm;
then add the cooked potatoes to
the remaining curry and stir gently
for a minute or two so that the
potatoes are well coated with the
spicy sauce.

7 Arrange the chosen accompaniment attractively around the edge
of each plate.

Curried haricot bean salad

This salad makes a substantial
supper dish on its own. But a small
portion can accompany cold meats for
a main meal; it goes particularly well
with lamb or chicken.

   Slimmer's portion:
   Calories: 265
     Carbohydrate
     units: 5½

SERVES 4
400 g [14 oz] canned haricot or
   flageolot beans
2 medium-sized tart dessert
   apples
1 garlic clove
salt
60 ml [4 tablespoons]
   vegetable oil
30 ml [2 tablespoons] cider
   vinegar
5 ml [1 teaspoon] curry paste
   or powder
30 ml [2 tablespoons] mango
   chutney
freshly ground black pepper
30 ml [2 tablespoons] chopped
   fresh coriander leaves
   (optional)

1 Drain the beans and put them into
a salad bowl. Quarter, core, then
finely chop the apples and add to
the beans.

2 Peel, then crush the garlic with
a little salt. Next, beat together the
oil, vinegar, curry and chutney.
Add the garlic, then fold the dressing into the salad. Season to
taste with salt and pepper. Sprinkle
over the chopped coriander, if
using.

Holiday cooking

Holidays are for enjoying, so you'll want to be out and about as much as you can. Don't tie yourself to the stove. Concentrate on quickly prepared food and, of course, salads and fresh fruit.

If renting a cottage or caravan in the country, make the most of local produce. Look for free-range eggs and fresh, home-grown fruit and vegetables—a real treat for the town dweller.

If you travel to a Mediterranean country for your holiday, you are almost certain to be near a market—an entertainment in itself.

Spare the olive oil and dress your salads with freshly squeezed lemon juice instead.

Ripe, juicy peaches, melons and other mouthwatering fruit are usually plentiful, so there should really be no problem in choosing a relatively 'non fattening' dessert.

In the food shops there will be an array of marvellous sausages, pâtés and cheeses. Provided that you are careful not to over-indulge, these new and different foods will make a

nice, refreshing change to your diet.

Holidaying by the sea, gives the opportunity to try the wide range of fish available. Take advantage of less familiar varieties as well as old favourites such as whiting and red and grey mullet.

Small extras to remember
- Take one efficient all-purpose knife with a serrated edge.
- For barbecues, take kebab skewers, picnic mugs, perhaps cocktail sticks—and a cloth to wipe sticky fingers!
- A good grater for cheese and raw vegetables is invaluable.
- A sieve will double as a colander.
- A non-stick frying-pan is a boon to a slimmer on holiday.
- A two-handled saucepan will also serve as a casserole.
- An insulated picnic bag is ideal for transporting prepared food for a well-organized start and for outings during the holiday. Also, buy freezing sachets to help keep food cool.

Venetian liver

An Italian classic, but if you can't face chopping the onions, the liver would be delicious served with plain boiled French beans and, for non-slimmers, potato crisps.

Slimmer's portion:
  Calories: 250
  Carbohydrate units: 2

SERVES 4
450 g [1 lb] calves' liver
450 g [1 lb] onions
15 ml [1 tablespoon] olive oil
salt
freshly ground black pepper
5 ml [1 teaspoon] butter
freshly chopped parsley to
  garnish

1 Peel, then slice the onions very finely.

2 Coat the bottom of a non-stick saucepan with the olive oil. Add the onions, cover the pan and stew for 10–15 minutes until tender. Check occasionally and stir with a wooden spatula so that the onions cook evenly.

3 In the meantime, trim and finely slice the liver, making the strips only 6 mm [¼"] thick. Season with salt and pepper.

4 Gently melt the butter in another non-stick frying-pan. Add the liver slices and sauté for 1–2 minutes, turning frequently.

5 To serve, arrange the onions on a warmed serving dish, place the liver slices on top and sprinkle over the chopped parsley.

Greek lamb fricassée

Although this dish takes an hour or so to cook, the preparation time is short and the result makes a welcome change. Serve with new baby carrots and plain boiled rice—slimmers should go easy with a small portion of rice.

Slimmer's portion, serving 4:
Calories: 525
Carbohydrate units: 3
Slimmer's portion, serving 6:
Calories: 350
Carbohydrate units: 2

SERVES 4–6
700 g [1½ lb] boned leg of lamb
700 g [1½ lb] onions
25 g [1 oz] butter
salt
freshly ground black pepper
1 large egg yolk
30 ml [2 tablespoons] lemon juice
15 ml [1 tablespoon] freshly chopped basil or mint

1 Trim all visible fat from the meat, then cut meat into cubes. Peel and slice the onions.

2 Melt the butter in a non-stick frying-pan, add the sliced onions, cover and cook gently for about 15 minutes, until soft but not brown. Check occasionally and stir to cook the onions evenly.

3 Add the meat to the pan, increase heat and brown on all sides. Skim off excess fat.

4 Stir in 150 ml [¼ pt] water and the seasoning. Bring to simmering point, then cover the pan and cook very gently for one hour, until the meat is tender.

5 Beat the egg yolk together with the lemon juice.

6 Using a slotted spoon, transfer meat to a serving dish and keep warm. Boil meat juices rapidly to reduce to about 275 ml [½ pt].

7 Add a few spoonfuls of the pan liquid to the egg and lemon mixture. Whisk well, then pour into the pan. Continue whisking over low heat until sauce begins to thicken. Take care not to let it boil or the sauce will curdle. Adjust seasoning.

8 Pour the thickened sauce over the meat and sprinkle with the herbs.

Variations
●For veal fricassée, substitute boned shoulder of veal. Omit the lemon juice and garnish with paprika. Serve with noodles and a green vegetable.
Slimmer's portion, serving 4:
  Calories: 465
  Carbohydrate units: 3
●For chicken fricassée, substitute chicken breast meat. Add one medium-sized red pepper, de-seeded and finely sliced, with the water and seasoning. Omit the lemon juice. Garnish with chopped parsley. Serve with a baked potato and undressed green salad.
Slimmer's portion, serving 4:
  Calories: 315
  Carbohydrate units: 3

Sweet and sour kebabs

The kebabs may be cooked on a grid over an open fire if wished. Serve them on a bed of finely shredded lettuce (no dressing will be needed) or you can use a bed of raw cabbage.

Slimmer's portion, serving 4:
Calories: 490
Carbohydrate units: 2
Slimmer's portion, serving 6:
Calories: 325
Carbohydrate units: 1½

SERVES 4–6 KEBABS
700 g [1½ lb] boned leg of lamb
1 large or 2 small onions
1 medium-sized green pepper
100 g [¼ lb] button mushrooms
100 g [¼ lb] canned pineapple chunks

1 garlic clove (optional)
a little vegetable oil

For the marinade:
5 ml [1 teaspoon] brown sugar
5 ml [1 teaspoon] salt
5 ml [1 teaspoon] ground ginger
75 ml [5 tablespoons] cider vinegar
20 ml [4 teaspoons] soy sauce
freshly ground black pepper

1 Trim off all visible fat from the lamb and cut the meat into 2.5 cm [1"] cubes. Spread out on a shallow dish.

2 Next, make the marinade. In a bowl, dissolve the sugar, salt and ginger in the vinegar. Add the soy sauce and pepper and mix well together.

3 Pour the marinade over the lamb. Cover the dish with foil and leave for several hours, or all day, in a cool place.

4 Heat the grill. Peel the onion(s), then cut into quarters and separate the layers. De-seed the pepper, then cut into 2.5 cm [1"] squares. Wipe the mushrooms, discard the stalks and, if large, cut in half or quarters. Drain the pineapple chunks.

5 Wipe each skewer with oil and, if wished, thread each through the garlic clove for added flavour. Discard the garlic. Next, thread the cubes of meat alternately with the onion sections, pepper squares, mushroom tops and the pineapple chunks.

6 Place across a grill pan and cook under medium grill 10–15 minutes, turning frequently and basting with the marinade.

Variation
●For Greek kebabs, marinate the lamb in olive oil, lemon juice and sliced onions, season to taste with salt, pepper and fresh or dried thyme, marjoram, basil or oregano. Cook as directed above.
Slimmer's portion, serving 4:
  Calories: 580
  Carbohydrate units: 1
Slimmer's portion, serving 6:
  Calories: 385
  Carbohydrate units: ½

Mero cristina

☒ *This recipe is named after a fish called meron, found off the shores of France. It is very similar to cod, which we have substituted here. Serve with a plain green vegetable and boiled new potatoes (slimmer's beware) or mange tout and the parsley salad—see salad suggestions on this page.*

Slimmer's portion:
  Calories: 220
  Carbohydrate units: 1

SERVES 4
4 × 225 g [½ lb] cod steaks
1 small onion
salt
freshly ground black pepper
juice of 1 medium-sized
  orange

To garnish:
1 medium-sized orange
freshly chopped parsley

1 Heat the oven to 150°C [300°F] gas mark 2. Rinse the cod steaks and pat dry with kitchen paper. Cut four squares of aluminium foil, large enough to wrap each cod steak. Peel, then chop the onion finely.

2 Place each cod steak in the centre of a piece of foil and put on a baking sheet. Season with salt and pepper. Divide the chopped onion between the four steaks and scatter on top of each.

3 Slightly lift the edges of the foil round each steak. Scatter the orange juice over each steak, putting an equal amount on each and taking care that none is lost.

4 Fold the aluminium foil over each steak, and seal the joins well.

5 Cook in the centre of the oven for 25–30 minutes. Meanwhile, pare the skin and white pith from the whole orange. Cut out the flesh segments, discarding any pips, and set aside.

6 Remove the parcels from the oven. With a fish slice, lift each carefully on to a warmed serving dish. Open the foil, lift the steak on to the serving dish and pour over the orange and onion sauce. Continue with each parcel, arranging the steaks overlapping.

7 Garnish with the orange segments and sprinkle over the parsley. Serve immediately.

SALAD SUGGESTIONS

● For lettuce and orange salad, finely shred lettuce and dress well with fresh orange juice, season with freshly ground black pepper.
Slimmer's portion, 100 g [4 oz]:
  Calories: 40
  Carbohydrate units: 1
● For carrot and nut salad, mix grated carrot with some ground hazelnuts and dress with lemon juice and freshly chopped parsley.
Slimmer's portion, 100 g [4 oz]:
  Calories: 75
  Carbohydrate units: 2
● For tomato salad, slice ripe tomatoes, salt lightly and drain. Dress with a little olive oil and lemon juice. Garnish with finely sliced onion and freshly chopped basil.
Slimmer's portion, 100 g [4 oz]:
  Calories: 80
  Carbohydrate units: 1
● For mushroom salad, finely slice raw field mushrooms, season with a little crushed garlic, if liked, and dress with olive oil and lemon juice. Garnish with fresh prawns or chopped hard-boiled egg.
Slimmer's portion, 100 g [4 oz]:
  Calories: 120
  without garnish: 80
  Carbohydrate units: 0
● For parsley salad, mix a generous amount of freshly chopped parsley with a small finely chopped onion, some finely sliced whole lemon and season with salt to taste.
Slimmer's portion, 100 g [4 oz]:
  Calories: 5
  Carbohydrate units: negligible
● For cucumber salad, dress peeled and diced cucumber with yoghurt and season to taste with salt and pepper.
Slimmer's portion, 100 g [4 oz]:
  Calories: 60
  Carbohydrate units: negligible
● For spinach salad, thoroughly wash young spinach leaves and a bunch of watercress, then trim stalks of both. Crumble a well-grilled rasher of streaky bacon over them, dress with cider vinegar and season with freshly ground nutmeg and black pepper.
Slimmer's portion, 100 g [4 oz]:
  Calories: 90
  Carbohydrate units: negligible

Summer salad

☒☒ *A colourful and unusual salad which provides a complete light meal and one with which you can ring the changes yourself according to the season.*

Slimmer's portion:
  Calories: 235
  Without the olives: 220
  Carbohydrate units: 3

SERVES 4
450 g [1 lb] young broad beans
one bunch of radishes
2 medium-sized oranges
4 medium-sized hard-boiled
  eggs
12 black olives, stoned
  (optional)
30 ml [2 tablespoons] olive oil
15 ml [1 tablespoon] lemon
  juice
salt
freshly ground black pepper

To garnish:
parsley sprigs

1 Remove the beans from the pod and put in a salad bowl.

2 Wash, then top and tail the radishes and slice thickly. Add to the broad beans.

3 Using a knife, cut the skin from the oranges, removing all the white pith. Divide the flesh into segments, discarding any pips. Add the orange segments to the salad bowl. Mix the beans, radishes and orange together.

4 Quarter the eggs and arrange in the bowl together with the stoned black olives, if using.

5 Beat the oil together with the lemon juice and salt and pepper to taste. Pour over the salad. Allow to stand for at least one hour before serving. Garnish with parsley sprigs.

SUGGESTIONS FOR SERVING FRESH FRUIT

Just as salt improves the flavour of savoury dishes, citrus juice will bring out the natural sweetness of fresh fruit. Experiment with mixtures of different fruits or try the following:
● For Julia's pears, quarter and core

fresh dessert pears and coat well with lemon juice. Non-slimmers may like the contrast in texture of a little sugar sprinkled over. But really ripe pears are sweet enough without this addition.

Slimmer's portion per 100 g [¼ lb] pear:

Calories: 35
Carbohydrate units: 2

●For Italian strawberries, rinse, drain and hull fresh strawberries. Coat berries thoroughly with fresh orange juice and chill well before serving.

Slimmer's portion, 100 g [¼ lb]:

Calories: 45
Carbohydrate units: 3½

●For tropical melon, slice an ogen or honeydew melon in half, and discard the seeds. Scoop out the flesh in neat spoonfuls. Mix well with fresh lime or grapefruit juice and return to melon shells. Chill and serve the dish garnished with sprigs of fresh mint.

Slimmer's portion, 100 g [¼ lb]:

Calories: 15
Carbohydrate units: 1½

Cheese is really excellent served with many fruits. Try these combinations:

●For figs à la greque, serve fresh ripe figs with a tart goat's cheese, such as Greek Fetta, or white Stilton.

Slimmer's portion per fig and 25 g [1 oz] cheese:

Calories: 105
Carbohydrate units: 1

●For French-style nectarines, serve fresh ripe nectarines with a portion of Camembert. The nectarines could be replaced by apricots.

Slimmer's portion per fruit and 25 g [1 oz] cheese:

Calories: 105
Carbohydrate units: ½

●For cerises Suisse, serve black cherries with Brie.

Slimmer's portion per 100 g [¼ lb] cherries and 25 g [1 oz] cheese:

Calories: 130
Carbohydrate units: 2

For a lunch in the sun, serve cool summer salad followed by blackberry fool. A nectarine served in the French style, with a lump of cheese, makes a perfect summer snack.

Blackberry fool

✕If the children bring blackberries from a country walk, try making this cool summery dessert. It is a good idea to use a thick yoghurt because this recipe has a fairly thin consistency.

Slimmer's portion:
Calories: 140
Carbohydrate units: 4

SERVES 4
450 g [1 lb] blackberries
400 ml [14 fl oz] low-fat natural yoghurt
25 g [1 oz] caster sugar

1 Rinse the blackberries carefully in cold water and then drain them. Pass the berries through a sieve into a bowl.

2 Mix the yoghurt into the resulting purée. Sweeten with the caster sugar.

3 Spoon the mixture into a large round serving dish. Chill well before serving.

Roger Phillips

Picnicking

Picnics and slimming don't exactly go together. Eating out of doors is such fun that it's all too easy to eat twice as much as usual.

The secret of successful picnics for slimmers is to choose the main dish with care so that it is well within the day's allowance. Non-slimmers can fill up with crisp French bread or rolls and butter.

Fresh fruit such as grapes, apples, pears and plums are the easiest desserts to take on a picnic—take cheese as well for a more substantial finish to the meal.

If you are preparing desserts, they must be packed in polythene containers for transporting to the spot where you will be eating. Yoghurt, jellies or little individual fruit pies are the things most likely to arrive at

Cheese and carrot quiche and crunchy picnic salad will be popular with all.

the picnic site safe and uncrushed.

Take fruit juice, dry white or rosé wine or the refreshing yoghurt drink Lassi (the recipe is given on page 42) to drink. Carry fruit juice or Lassi in a well chilled vacuum flask to keep it cool. Keep the wine in its bottle and if there is a cool stream near your picnic spot pop the bottle in the water for a few minutes so that it will have a chance to chill.

If the family is fond of picnics and likely to spring one on you at a moment's notice, don't get caught short of the slimmer's diet requirements.

Always keep a good stock of fruit, salad ingredients, cold meat and cottage cheese at the ready for every fine weather weekend and all through the school holidays. Then, if you haven't time to prepare one of these lovely recipes, you can at worst make up sandwiches for non-slimmers and still have something tasty in the picnic basket to satisfy those watching their weight.

'Sandwiches' made from pitta bread are excellent picnic food. While slightly high in Calorific value and CU, they are simple and quick to make, neat and easy to carry and eat.

Cheese and carrot quiche

This is a lovely moist quiche, ideal for a summer picnic as it can be carried in its flan tin, wrapped in foil. The weight of the pastry used is the weight of the flour to make it—not the made weight.

Slimmer's portion, serving 4:
   Calories: 405
   Carbohydrate units: 6½
Slimmer's portion, serving 6:
   Calories: 270
   Carbohydrate units: 4

SERVES 4–6
150 g [5 oz] shortcrust pastry
50 g [2 oz] mature Cheddar
100 g [¼ lb] young carrots

50 g [2 oz] onion
1 large egg
90 ml [6 tablespoons] thin
   cream
a pinch of nutmeg
salt and pepper
parsley to garnish

1 Heat the oven to 200°C [400°F] gas mark 6.

2 Roll out the pastry and use to line a 20 cm [8"] flan tin. Bake the pastry blind for 10 minutes.

3 Coarsely grate the cheese. Scrub, then grate the carrots. Peel, then finely chop the onion. Mix well together in a bowl and then spoon into the pastry case.

4 Beat the egg and stir in the cream. Add a pinch of nutmeg and season to taste with salt and pepper. Beat with a wooden spoon until the mixture is smooth.

5 Pour the creamy custard mixture over the carrot filling. Return the flan to the oven and bake for 25 minutes. Garnish with parsley.

Stuffed eggs

Hard-boiled eggs are always a picnic favourite. Here they are given a touch of luxury with a filling of creamy cod's roe. Instructions for making slimmer's mayonnaise are given on page 17. If using fresh cod's roe, remove the tough outer skin in the following way: cover the roe in boiling water and leave to stand for 1 minute. Drain, then peel away the skin with a sharp knife.

Slimmer's portion:
   Calories: 100
   Carbohydrate units: 0

SERVES 4
4 medium-sized hard-boiled
   eggs
25 g [1 oz] fresh or canned
   smoked cod's roe
30 ml [2 tablespoons]
   slimmers' mayonnaise
5 ml [1 teaspoon] freshly
   snipped chives
salt and pepper
paprika
4 large lettuce leaves

1 Shell the hard-boiled eggs, then cut each one in half lengthways.

2 Use a small spoon to scoop out the yolks then rub the yolks through a sieve into a small bowl. Reserve.

3 Rub the cod's roe through a sieve, then pound it with the mayonnaise to a smooth paste. Gradually blend in the sieved yolks. Add the chives and season to taste.

4 Pack the filling into the egg white cavities and smooth it over the cut surface.

5 Then re-shape the eggs, pressing the halves together so that they stick together and there is a band of filling in the middle.

6 Wrap each egg in a crisp lettuce leaf and pack in a small polythene container. The lettuce leaf will keep the egg cool and act as a napkin when eating.

Picnic salad

Use firm tomatoes and then this salad will travel well and stay crisp and fresh no matter how warm the day. Pack in a polythene container and provide forks for eating.

Slimmer's portion:
   Calories: 110
   Carbohydrate units: 1

SERVES 4
100 g [¼ lb] young carrots
100 g [¼ lb] tomatoes
1 small cauliflower
15 ml [1 tablespoon] white
   wine vinegar
2.5 ml [½ teaspoon] French
   mustard
salt
freshly ground black pepper
45 ml [3 tablespoons]
   vegetable oil
1 garlic clove, peeled

1 Scrub the carrots, then cut into thin strips. Cut the tomatoes into wedges.

2 Wash the cauliflower thoroughly, then break it into very small florets.

3 To make the dressing, put the vinegar into a small bowl, cup or jug. Add the mustard and seasonings to taste. Stir well with a fork

to blend. Pour in the oil and beat vigorously to mix and thicken. Using a garlic press, squeeze the juice from the garlic directly into the dressing.

4 Mix the vegetables in a bowl and pour over the oil and vinegar dressing. Toss well so that all the salad is coated.

Sweet and sour spare ribs

These spare ribs are delicious either hot for a supper dish or cold to take on a picnic. (To carry, simply wrap parcels of three ribs in foil.) Serve with a fresh green salad.

Slimmer's portion:
   Calories: 380
   Carbohydrate units: 1½

SERVES 4
12–20 spare ribs, according to
   size
45 ml [3 tablespoons] thin
   honey
1 garlic clove
30 ml [2 tablespoons] soy
   sauce
30 ml [2 tablespoons] lemon
   juice
2.5 ml [½ teaspoon] ground
   ginger
2.5 ml [½ teaspoon] ground
   cinnamon
salt
freshly ground black pepper

1 Heat the oven to 190°C [375°F] gas mark 5.

2 Arrange the ribs in the bottom of an ovenproof dish. Cook near the top of the oven for 35 minutes, turning the ribs once. (Do not cover the dish for cooking.)

3 Meanwhile, warm the honey in a small saucepan. Peel, then finely chop the garlic and add to the pan together with the soy sauce, lemon juice, ginger and cinnamon. Season with salt and pepper.

4 Remove the ribs from the oven and pour off the fat, then pour over the warm honey sauce.

5 Return the dish to the oven and cook the ribs, uncovered, for a further 25 minutes, turning once or twice so that they brown on both sides.

Two picnic treats—orange cups and lassi.

Spicy stuffed tomatoes

☒ *To transport these stuffed tomatoes, pack close together in a single layer in a polythene container. If the container is too large, put each tomato in a pastry cutter to prevent rolling around.*

For a main course meal, serve the tomatoes with ham and celery parcels (95 Calories, 0 Carbohydrate units each). Cut some celery sticks the same length as the ham. Fill the celery sticks with a seasoned cottage cheese, then sandwich two sticks together and roll up inside a slice of ham. Secure with a cocktail stick to prevent unwrapping and pack close together in a polythene container.

Slimmer's portion:
 Calories: 175
 Carbohydrate units: 2

SERVES 4
4 large tomatoes
1 medium-sized ripe avocado
15 ml [1 tablespoon] lemon juice
a pinch of chilli powder
quarter of a green pepper, finely chopped
salt
freshly ground pepper
5 ml [1 teaspoon] freshly chopped parsley

1 Cut a thin slice from the top of each tomato and reserve. Scoop out the pulp and discard.

2 Cut the avocado in half, remove the stone, then scoop out the flesh.

3 Put the flesh in a bowl, add the lemon juice and chilli powder and mash with a fork until well blended. Stir in the chopped pepper.

4 Season to taste, then pack into the hollowed-out tomato cases. Sprinkle a little parsley on top of the filling. Then cover with the reserved lids.

Orange cups

☒ *These make a lovely portable treat to take on a picnic.*

If you want to serve them for a dinner party, pile the creamy orange mixture into individual glass dishes instead of the orange shells and decorate with sprigs of fresh mint or lemon balm.

Make the vanilla-flavoured custard sauce according to instructions on page 13, cover to prevent a skin forming and leave to cool before using.

Slimmer's portion:
 Calories: 95
 Carbohydrate units: 2½

SERVES 4
150 ml [¼ pt] vanilla-flavoured egg custard
4 medium-sized oranges
about 30 ml [2 tablespoons] unsweetened orange juice
15 g [½ oz] gelatine
50 ml [2 fl oz] whipping cream
mint leaves to garnish

1 Slice the top third from each orange. Grate the zest from the tops and reserve. Squeeze the juice from the tops into a measuring jug.

2 Using a grapefruit spoon, scoop out the flesh from the rest of the oranges. Set orange shells aside.

3 Extract the juice from the orange flesh by pressing through a sieve, then pour into the measuring jug and add enough unsweetened orange juice to bring the liquid up to 225 ml [8 fl oz].

4 Put 60 ml [4 tablespoons] of the orange juice into a heavy based pan and reserve. Stir the remainder into the cold egg custard together with the reserved zest.

5 Sprinkle the gelatine over the orange juice in the pan and leave to soak for 5 minutes. Then dissolve over very low heat without stirring.

6 Pour the dissolved gelatine in a thin stream into the egg custard, stirring constantly until well mixed. Then put aside until just on the point of setting.

7 Lightly whip the cream, then fold it into the almost set orange custard.

8 Spoon the creamy mixture into the orange shells and leave in a cold place for about 1 hour or until set. Garnish with mint.

Lassi

☒ *Lassi is a drink of Indian origin and very cooling on a hot summer's day. Take it to the picnic in a chilled vacuum flask.*

Calories: 85
Carbohydrate units: ½

SERVES 1
150 ml [¼ pt] low-fat natural yoghurt
1.5 ml [¼ teaspoon] salt
1.5 ml [¼ teaspoon] ground nutmeg
1.5 ml [¼ teaspoon] ground cloves
1.5 ml [¼ teaspoon] ground cinnamon
1.5 ml [¼ teaspoon] ground ginger

1 Turn the yoghurt into a mixing bowl. Using a fork or whisk, beat in enough water—approximately 150 ml [¼ pt]—to give the consistency of milk.

2 Add the salt and sweet spices to the thinned yoghurt.

3 Pour into a jug and chill in the refrigerator for at least 2 hours.

ENTERTAINING

When your friends start to notice you are slimming, show off your improved figure by giving a dinner party! With these delicious, well-balanced meals, they will never guess that the Calories or carbohydrates have been carefully calculated to suit the slimmer.

Formal dinner for 4

This menu shows just how sophisticated 'diet' food can be. The dishes chosen are not difficult to prepare and are very tempting. The celery can cook in the oven on the shelf beneath the duckling. Broccoli spears and baby new potatoes take only 10 minutes to cook. Put them into separate pans of boiling salted water just before you serve the first course so they will be ready by the time you come to eat the main course. Alternatively, you could cook them ahead of time and keep warm in the oven with the roasting bird.

If you wish, after the dessert and to top-off the meal, serve a cheeseboard with fresh fruit. Include Camembert and Edam cheese for the slimmers.

As far as the wine is concerned— one 125 ml [4 fl oz] glass (which is smaller than a standard-size glass) of claret or Côtes du Rhône, will 'cost' you 80 Calories or 4 carbohydrate units. Omit the Sauterne entirely—this is 100 Calories or 5 carbohydrate units for a 125 ml [4 fl oz] glass. If you end the meal with coffee, take it black and unsugared.

Roger Phillips

Menu

Calorie content per portion		Carbo-hydrate units per portion
130	Smoked mackerel pâté served with hot	10
*60	wholemeal toast	*2½
375	Roast duckling with plum sauce	2
20	Broccoli spears	neg
30	Oven-braised celery	neg
*80	Baby new potatoes	*4
75	Swiss pears ·	3
*90	Cheeseboard	0
0	Black coffee	0
	To drink:	
80	Côtes du Rhône or St Emilion with main course and cheese.	4
*100	Sauterne with dessert	*5
1,040		20½

Food that the slimmer should avoid. Totals without these will be: Calories: 710 Carbohydrate units: 9

Countdown timetable

TWO DAYS BEFORE THE MEAL
Roast duckling with plum sauce: if using frozen duck, remember to allow 36–48 hours for it to thaw.

THE DAY BEFORE THE MEAL
Do the shopping.
Smoked mackerel pâté: prepare the pâté and store in refrigerator overnight — steps 1–3.

ON THE DAY OF THE MEAL
In the morning
Swiss pears: prepare, poach and transfer from pan to serving dish — steps 1–4.
Scrub the baby new potatoes; divide the broccoli into spears. Prepare the garnish.

In the afternoon
Lay the table.

3½ hours before the meal
Roast duckling with plum sauce: prepare duckling for roasting — step 2 — and simmer giblets with water for 1 hour — step 4.

2½ hours before the meal
Roast duckling with plum sauce: heat the oven — step 1. Strain the stock and make the plum purée — steps 5–7.

2 hours before the meal
Roast duckling with plum sauce: roast the duckling — step 3.

1½ hours before the meal
Oven-braised celery: prepare, put in

the oven to braise — see recipe on page 28, steps 2–5.
Cheeseboard: set out the cheese selection. Get yourself ready.

15 minutes before the meal
Roast duckling with plum sauce: remove duckling from oven and transfer to warmed serving dish. Lower oven temperature to very low and return duckling to oven to keep warm. Complete plum sauce, transfer to warmed sauce-boat and keep warm — step 8–9.
Wholemeal toast: toast the bread and wrap in napkin to keep warm.
Smoked mackerel pâté: arrange on serving plates, then put the pâté on the table — step 4.

Just before serving the first course
Broccoli spears and baby new potatoes: put on to cook in boiling salted water.

Between first and main courses
Roast duckling with plum sauce: garnish duckling with watercress and the plum halves and garnish the sauce with chopped parsley. Serve — step 10.
Broccoli spears and baby new potatoes: drain both vegetables, dish up and serve.
Oven-braised celery: remove from oven and serve.

Between main course and dessert
Swiss pears: top pears with yoghurt and muesli — step 5.
Make the coffee.

Smoked mackerel pâté

This is a creamy, rich-tasting fish pâté. Variations can be made using canned tuna (300 Calories) or sardines in tomato sauce (230 Calories). Serve with wholemeal toast to non-slimmers and pass butter separately. If you do not have a blender, mash the fish with a fork before adding the other ingredients.

Slimmer's portion:
Calories: 130
Carbohydrate units: 0

SERVES 4
200 g (7 oz) smoked mackerel fillets
half a lemon
15 ml (1 tablespoon) low-fat natural yoghurt
5 ml (1 teaspoon) horseradish sauce
salt
freshly ground black pepper

To garnish:
4 lettuce leaves
half a cucumber, thinly sliced

1 Grate the zest from half a lemon, set aside and squeeze the juice.

2 Cut the fish fillets into small pieces and put in a blender with the lemon juice. Blend until smooth.

3 Scrape the blended fish into a bowl, then stir in the lemon zest together with the yoghurt and horseradish. Cover and store in the refrigerator.

4 To serve, wash the lettuce leaves

and arrange on four plates with the slices of cucumber. Divide the pâté mixture equally between the four servings.

Roast duckling with plum sauce

Duckling roasted on a rack loses much of its fat, as the fat drips down into the pan beneath.

Slimmer's portion of duck:
Calories: 350
Carbohydrate units: 0
Slimmer's portion of plum sauce:
Calories: 25
Carbohydrate units: 2

SERVES 4
2.3 kg [5 lb] duckling
salt
freshly ground black pepper

For the plum sauce:
30 ml [2 tablespoons] brandy
225 g [½ lb] cooking plums

To garnish:
1 bunch watercress, prepared
4 dessert plums, halved and stoned
chopped parsley

1 Place shelf in centre and heat oven to 220°C [425°F] gas mark 7.

2 Remove any solid white fat from the cavity of the bird, then rinse under cold water inside and out. Pat dry. Season the cavity with salt and pepper; prick skin with a fork. Truss bird with string.

3 Place the duckling on a rack in a roasting tin. Roast in oven for 15 minutes, then reduce heat to 180°C [350°F] gas mark 4 and cook for a further 1½ hours. Twenty minutes before the end of roasting time, turn the bird to brown its back. Turn it breast-side up again 5 minutes before the end of roasting.

4 In the meantime, put the giblets in a saucepan, cover with 425 ml [¾ pt] water and simmer, covered, for 1 hour. Strain giblet stock. Wash and stone the plums.

5 Put the stock in a saucepan together with the brandy. Heat gently for a few minutes, then add the stoned plums. Simmer for 10 minutes, or until the plums are soft.

6 Remove the plums from the heat and allow to cool slightly. Blend in a liquidizer or pass through a sieve to make a purée. Check seasoning and set aside.

7 At the end of cooking time, test if the duckling is cooked by piercing the thick part of a leg with a skewer. The juices should run clear. Transfer the cooked duckling to a warmed serving dish. Remove string; keep bird warm.

8 Pour off the fat from the roasting tin, then pour in plum purée. Set tin over a low heat. Heat sauce stirring roasting juices into the purée. Check seasoning. Boil for 5 minutes to thicken slightly.

9 Garnish duck with watercress and plums. Pour sauce into a sauceboat; sprinkle parsley over.

Swiss pears

These dessert pears are served at room temperature with a topping.

Slimmer's portion:
Calories: 75
Carbohydrate units: 3

SERVES 4
4 dessert pears
15 ml [1 tablespoon] lemon juice
finely grated lemon zest of half a lemon
1 cinnamon stick
3 drops of artificial sweetener
125 ml [4 fl oz] low-fat natural yoghurt
20 ml [4 teaspoons] muesli or fruit bran

1 Peel pears and cut in half lengthways. Remove woody stem and scoop out centre core with a spoon. Put pear halves in a saucepan and pour over 150 ml [¼ pt] water and the lemon juice. Add the lemon zest and cinnamon stick.

2 Cover and simmer pears until just soft—about 15 minutes.

3 Carefully remove pears from pan and arrange in a serving dish. Discard cinnamon stick. Then sweeten the cooking liquid with artificial liquid sweetener to taste. Pour the liquid over the pears then leave until cold.

4 Just before serving, top each pear with some natural yoghurt and sprinkle over some muesli or fruit bran. Serve immediately.

Roger Phillips

Menu

Calorie content per portion		Carbo-hydrate units per portion
50	Chilled watercress soup	1
180	Cold salmon trout	0
30	Slimmers' green mayonaise	neg
*205	Basic blender tarragon mayonnaise	0
105	Stuffed tomatoes	1
*125	Apple, celery and walnut salad	1½
40	Cucumber jelly mould	1
20	Special green salad	½
*40	Cold minted new potatoes	*2
*125	Macédoine of summer fruit	*3
65	Raspberry cream	2½
25	with almond tuiles	½
90	Cheeseboard	0
0	Black coffee	0
1,100		13½
	To drink:	
75	Pouilly Fumé with first 2 courses	4
*85	Sauterne with dessert	*4½
100	OR Champagne (Brut) with whole meal	5
160 or 100		8½ or 5
Total: 1,260 or 1,200		22 or 18

*Food and drink that the slimmer should avoid. By being selective, the totals can be reduced to:
Calories: 605 plus drink
Carbohydrate units: 8 plus drink

Buffet lunch for 12

If you are entertaining more guests than you can seat comfortably around your dining table, a buffet-style meal, which allows guests to help themselves, is the answer.

It's difficult for the slimmer not to nibble when preparing a meal of this size — a lot of will-power is needed to resist. To avoid temptation, munch apple, carrot or celery instead.

As the party is bound to be a special occasion, it seems unfair for the slimmer not to sample all the delicious dishes prepared. Although the food is not very fattening, generous helpings of everything will upset the count for the day. Take 'slimming' portions and be selective — the menu card guides you on things to avoid. If necessary, eat less the next day to even out the count.

Some dishes can be prepared well ahead and frozen, which saves a lot of time and effort close to the party. These include the watercress soup, almond tuiles and raspberry cream. Order the salmon trout at least a week ahead from a reliable fishmonger to make sure you get one.

TWO DAYS BEFORE
Do the shopping.
Almond tuiles: make and bake. Store in an airtight tin—steps 1–6.
Slimmers' green mayonnaise (see variation on page 17): make double the quantity and store, covered, in the refrigerator—step 1.
Basic blender tarragon mayonnaise: make and store, covered, in the refrigerator—steps 1–4.
Apple, celery and walnut salad: make the dressing and store, covered, in the refrigerator—step 1.
Special green salad: make the dressing and store covered in the refrigerator—step 1.
Prepare parsley, mint and watercress for garnishing and store in polythene bags in the refrigerator.
Macédoine of summer fruit: toast almonds and store in an airtight tin—step 1.

THE DAY BEFORE
In the morning
Cucumber jelly mould: make the cucumber jelly and prepare the radish decorations—steps 1–13.
Cold salmon trout: prepare and poach the fish. Remove the skin and cover loosely with foil. Store in the refrigerator—steps 1–8.

In the afternoon
Chilled watercress soup: make and chill—steps 1–4.
Raspberry cream: make and pour into serving dishes. Chill in refrigerator—steps 1–5.
Apple, celery and walnut salad: chop celery and nuts and store in polythene bags in the refrigerator—step 2.
Special green salad: prepare vegetables and store in polythene bags in refrigerator—steps 2–5.
If using frozen food, remember to remove from the freezer to allow for thawing.

ON THE DAY
3½ hours before
Macédoine of summer fruit: prepare fruit and chill—steps 2–5.
Stuffed tomatoes: prepare tomatoes and make stuffing—steps 1–3.
Lay the table.
Stuffed tomatoes: stuff and garnish—steps 4–6.
Cold minted new potatoes: drain eight 270 g [10 oz] cans of new potatoes. Put in a large serving dish and garnish with chopped mint.
Cheeseboard: set out cheese (preferably a selection of Edam, Brie, Gouda and White Stilton) and place biscuits in a napkin-lined basket.
Slimmers' green mayonnaise and basic blender tarragon mayonnaise: spoon into sauce-boats.

2 hours before
Cold salmon trout: garnish—step 9.
Apple, celery and walnut salad: prepare apples—step 3.
Macédoine of summer fruit: sprinkle over almonds—step 6.
Raspberry cream: garnish—step 6.
Special green salad: mix non-leafy vegetables and dress—step 6.
Go and get changed.

1 hour before
Cucumber jelly mould: unmould and garnish—steps 14–15.
Special green salad: complete—step 7.
Apple, celery and walnut salad: mix salad and dress—step 4.
Almond tuiles: arrange on plate.

30 minutes before
Arrange all dishes (except for the soup) and sauce-boats on table. Greet guests.

5 minutes before
Chilled watercress soup: garnish with watercress and serve—step 5.

Chilled watercress soup

☒☒ *Spicy but cool, this creamy soup is the perfect start to a party, but it must be made ahead so that it is completely chilled before serving. Serve with French bread for non-slimmers.*

Slimmer's portion:
Calories: 50
Carbohydrate units: 1

SERVES 12
6 bunches of watercress
2.3 L [4 pt] chicken stock
90 ml [6 tablespoons] dried onion flakes
100 g [4 oz] skimmed milk powder
salt and pepper

1 Wash the watercress and trim away the coarser stems and any yellowing leaves. Save a few leaves for the garnish, then chop the rest roughly and put into a large saucepan.

2 Pour in the chicken stock and sprinkle in the dried onion flakes. Bring to the boil, cover and simmer for 15 minutes.

3 Remove the pan from the heat and allow to cool. Blend small quantities of soup at a time in a liquidizer, or pass through a sieve. Sprinkle in milk powder, whisking all the time. Pour into a large serving bowl.

4 Adjust seasoning, then pour into large serving bowl. Chill well.

5 To serve, garnish with a few whole watercress leaves.

Cold salmon trout
☒☒☒ *This is a luxury dish that is ideal for the weight-conscious, as 25 g [1 oz] of it is only 45 Calories and the carbohydrate content is negligible. A slimmer's portion should weigh 100 g [¼ lb].*

For non-slimmers or low-carbohydrate slimmers, the blender tarragon mayonnaise given on page 48 makes a delicious accompaniment to this dish, but for low-Calorie slimmers, the refreshing slimmer's green mayonnaise given as a variation on page 17 is equally good.

Slimmer's portion:
Calories: 180
Carbohydrate units: 0

SERVES 12
1 fresh salmon trout, weighing 2.3–2.7 kg [5–6 lb]

For the court-bouillon:
575 ml [1 pt] dry white wine

4 black peppercorns
1 small carrot, scrubbed and
   sliced
1 small onion, peeled and
   studded with 6 cloves
30 ml [2 tablespoons] wine
   vinegar
1 bay leaf
10 ml [2 teaspoons] salt

For the garnish:
cucumber slices
1 radish, trimmed and thinly
   sliced
watercress

1 Clean and prepare the fish: trim
  the fins, wash the whole fish well
  in cold water and scrape away any
  blood. Remove the gills if this has
  not been done by the fishmonger,
  but leave on the head and tail.

2 To make the court-bouillon, crush
  the peppercorns coarsely. Put all
  the ingredients in a large saucepan and pour in 1.1 L [2 pt] water.
  Heat to simmering point and simmer, uncovered, for 30 minutes.
  Allow to cool.

3 Place the fish in a fish kettle, or
  on a rack standing in a large
  roasting tin, and pour over the
  prepared court-bouillon to barely
  cover the fish.

4 Cover—with foil if using a roasting
  tin—and simmer very gently allow-
  ing 8 minutes per 450 g [1 lb].

5 Allow the fish to cool in the court-
  bouillon and then, when almost
  cold, transfer the fish carefully to
  a large sheet of damp greaseproof paper on a flat surface.

6 Using a sharp knife, cut the skin
  across the tail, around the head
  and down the length of the back-
  bone. Peel off the skin with the
  knife and scrape away any brown
  flesh from along the middle of the
  fish.

7 Using the greaseproof paper, roll
  the fish over and repeat the skin-
  ning process on the underside.

8 Transfer the whole fish to a large
  serving dish, using two fish slices.

9 Garnish the fish with thin slices
  of cucumber and radishes. Decorate the dish with watercress.

*Stuffed tomatoes, cucumber jelly and mixed
salads make impressive buffet-party fare.*

Basic blender mayonnaise

*This is an excellent basic mayon-
naise which low-carbohydrate slimmers can indulge in. It can be flavoured
as wished for different dishes and it
can be stored in the refrigerator for up
to a week. Use a jar with a plastic
screw-top lid—a metal lid may taint
the mayonnaise and give it an unpleasant flavour. To make a larger quantity
blend a second batch separately.*

Slimmer's portion:
   Calories: 205
   Carbohydrate units: 0

SERVES 6
1 medium-sized egg
**5 ml [1 teaspoon] mustard
   powder**
2.5 ml [½ teaspoon] salt
**1.5 ml [¼ teaspoon] cayenne
   pepper**
**30 ml [2 tablespoons] lemon
   juice**
225 ml [8 fl oz] peanut oil

1 Break the egg into the liquidizer.
  Add the mustard, salt, cayenne

and lemon juice. Pour in 50 ml [2
fl oz] of oil and blend for 1 minute.

2 Add another 50 ml [2 fl oz] of oil
  and blend for 1 minute.

3 Add the remaining 125 ml [4 fl oz]
  of oil and blend until smooth.

4 Pour into a suitable container and
  refrigerate until required.

Variations

● For tarragon mayonnaise to go
with salmon, add 5–10 ml [1–2 tea-
spoons] finely chopped fresh tarragon and parsley.

● For seafood cocktail sauce add
tomato relish and Worcestershire
sauce to taste.

● For curry dressing to go with cold
chicken or white fish, add curry paste
to taste and a little turmeric for extra
colour.

Stuffed tomatoes

*These creamy centred tomatoes are
decorated with slivers of olive.*

Slimmer's portion, 2 tomatoes:
   Calories: 105
   Carbohydrate units: 1

Roger Phillips

grated zest of 1 lemon
salt
freshly ground black pepper

1 To make the dressing, beat the yoghurt together with the honey, lemon juice and zest and seasonings to taste. Set on one side.

2 Scrub and finely chop the celery, then chop the nuts.

3 Core and dice the apples and turn each batch in the 45 ml [3 tablespoons] lemon juice until thoroughly coated to prevent discoloration.

4 Drain the apples and mix together with the celery and nuts. Toss in the dressing and serve garnished with chopped parsley.

Cucumber jelly

Cool and shiny, this attractive dish gives a party air with the minimum of expense. The crunchy radishes, cut into attractive roses, provide an excellent contrast to the smooth jelly.

Slimmer's portion:
Calories: 40
Carbohydrate units: 1

SERVES 12
450 g [1 lb] cucumber
salt
120 ml [8 tablespoons] lemon juice
150 ml [¼ pt] white wine vinegar or cider vinegar
1 small slice of onion
90 ml [6 tablespoons] sugar
25 g [1 oz] gelatine
a few drops of green food colouring
pepper

For the garnish:
12 small radishes, trimmed
a crisp lettuce heart

1 Cut about 18 thin slices from the cucumber. Salt them lightly, then set aside.

2 Peel, then chop the remaining cucumber. Put the chopped cucumber into a saucepan and add the lemon juice, vinegar, onion and sugar. Cook uncovered, over low heat until soft.

SERVES 12
24 small tomatoes
salt
175 g [6 oz] cream cheese (with or without chives)
175 g [6 oz] curd cheese
60 ml [4 tablespoons] low-fat natural yoghurt
freshly ground black pepper

For the garnish:
6 black olives, stoned and sliced into quarters
watercress

1 Wash the tomatoes, then cut a thin slice off each one at the stalk end.

2 Scoop out flesh and seeds from the centres with a spoon, taking care not to break the skin. Sprinkle the cavities with salt, then turn the tomatoes upside down to drain for 30 minutes. Rinse and pat dry.

3 Put the cheeses into a bowl. Beat together until softened, then gradually beat in the yoghurt. Season to taste with salt and pepper.

4 Spoon the cheese mixture into a large piping bag fitted with a 12 mm [½"] fluted vegetable nozzle.

5 Pipe the cheese mixture into the tomato cavities, then garnish each stuffed tomato with a slice of black olive.

6 Place the stuffed tomatoes in the centre of a serving plate and arrange watercress round them.

Apple, celery and walnut salad

This crunchy salad is an excellent foil for cold meat or fish.

Slimmer's portion:
Calories: 125
Carbohydrate units: 1½

SERVES 12
2 celery heads
175 g [6 oz] walnuts, shelled
6 red dessert apples
45 ml [3 tablespoons] lemon juice
chopped parsley to garnish

For the dressing:
275 ml [½ pt] low-fat natural yoghurt
15 ml [1 tablespoon] honey
30 ml [2 tablespoons] lemon juice

3 Remove from the heat. Allow to cool slightly then purée in a liquidizer or pass through a sieve.

4 Measure the purée and make up to 1.1 L [2 pt] with cold water.

5 Pour 60 ml [4 tablespoons] of the cucumber liquid into a small saucepan. Sprinkle over gelatine and allow to soak for 5 minutes. Then dissolve over a low heat, without stirring.

6 Pour the melted gelatine in a thin stream into the remaining cucumber liquid, stirring constantly until well mixed. Stir in the green colouring and season to taste. Leave to cool.

7 Put a 1.1 L [2 pt] ring mould into the freezer or freezer compartment of the refrigerator to get cold, then rinse in cold water.

8 When the jelly is almost on the point of setting (it should be the consistency of unbeaten egg white) spoon a little into the bottom of the mould.

9 Rinse the reserved cucumber slices, then dry on kitchen paper.

Arrange them overlapping in the bottom of the mould over the layer of jelly. Spoon over a little more jelly and put the mould into the freezer or freezer compartment of the refrigerator for a few minutes to set.

10 Add the remaining jelly and float any remaining cucumber slices on top. Put the jelly in the refrigerator, make sure it is standing level and leave to set.

11 To make radish roses, half way down the side of each radish make a downward slice towards the stem, to form a slit.

12 Make a second vertical slit, above the first one. Repeat this cutting action round the whole radish.

13 Put the cut radishes in a bowl filled with iced water. Leave to soak while the jelly sets. The cuts will open to make petals.

14 To turn out the jelly, dip the mould, up to the rim, in a basin full of hot water. Invert on to a wetted serving dish and give a sharp shake. Lift off the mould and wipe away any excess liquid.

15 Drain the radish roses. Fill the centre of the mould with leaves from the lettuce heart and the radish roses.

Special green salad

This salad, with its different shades of green, adds a bright, fresh touch to any buffet table.

Slimmer's portion:
 Calories: 20
 Carbohydrate units: ½

SERVES 12
2 large cos lettuce
2 bunches of watercress
1 medium-sized green pepper
225 g [½ lb] courgettes
225 g [½ lb] small leeks
150 g [5 oz] peas, fresh, or frozen OR broad beans
chopped parsley to garnish

For the dressing:
5 ml [1 teaspoon] English mustard powder
125 ml [4 fl oz] cider vinegar
3 drops of liquid artificial sweetener
salt
freshly ground black pepper

1 To make the dressing, blend the mustard together with the vinegar. Add the sweetener and salt and pepper to taste and beat well with a fork. Set aside until required.

2 Wash, then dry the lettuce. Tear the leaves into bite-sized pieces. Remove the stalks from the watercress, then wash and dry.

3 Core and de-seed the pepper and cut into thin slices. Wash the courgettes; top and tail, then cut into wafer-thin slices.

4 Trim the leeks, wash thoroughly then slice very finely.

5 Pod fresh peas or broad beans. Boil until cooked but still firm. If using broad beans, remove the grey-green bitter shell by squeezing each bean between your fingers so that the bright green centre pops out. Cool completely.

6 Put all the non-leafy vegetables into a salad bowl. Pour over the dressing and toss.

7 Just before serving, add the lettuce and watercress, toss thoroughly and sprinkle over the chopped parsley.

Macedoine of summer fruit

Wine adds a touch of luxury to fresh fruit salad and is no more fattening than the traditional syrup (a little of which is also included in this recipe). Provide cream for non-Calorie slimmers, if wished.

**Slimmer's portion:
Calories: 125
Carbohydrate units: 3½**

SERVES 12
100 g [¼ lb] flaked almonds
275 ml [½ pt] medium dry
    white wine
225 g [½ lb] fresh strawberries
225 g [½ lb] fresh raspberries
425 g [15 oz] canned black
    cherries, stoned
2 red dessert apples
2 large bananas

1 Toast the almonds, then set aside.

2 Pour the wine into a serving bowl and add 575 ml [1 pt] water.

3 Wash and drain all the fresh fruit. Hull the strawberries and raspberries and place in the wine.

4 Stir the canned cherries and their syrup into the bowl of wine and fresh fruit.

5 Core and slice the apples; peel and slice the bananas. Add to the rest of the fruit in the bowl and chill in the refrigerator.

6 Just before serving, sprinkle toasted almonds over the fruit salad.

Raspberry cream

Make two batches of this foamy pink pudding; one will serve eight, but allow for second helpings as it is very popular.

**Slimmer's portion:
Calories: 65
Carbohydrate units: 2½**

SERVES 8
900 g [2 lb] fresh raspberries
    (or frozen fruit, thawed)
25 ml [5 teaspoons] gelatine
175 ml [6 fl oz] canned
    evaporated milk, chilled
2 medium-sized egg whites
sprigs of mint for decoration

1 Hull the raspberries, then rinse in cold water. Reserve 8 of the best and purée the remainder in a blender or pass through a sieve. (You should have 575 ml [1 pt] of purée.)

2 Measure 225 ml [8 fl oz] water. Pour 60 ml [4 tablespoons] of the water into a heavy-based pan, sprinkle over the gelatine and leave to soak for 5 minutes. Heat gently, without stirring, until dissolved.

3 Stir the remaining water into the fruit purée. Pour the dissolved gelatine in a thin stream into the fruit purée, stirring constantly until well mixed. Chill in the refrigerator.

4 When the jelly is on the point of setting, add the evaporated milk. Using an electric beater or hand whisk, beat the mixture until thickened and foamy.

5 Using a clean whisk, beat the egg whites in a separate bowl until stiff, then fold into the foaming jelly. Pour into individual glass dishes and leave in a cold place for about 30 minutes or until set.

6 To serve, decorate with the reserved whole raspberries and sprigs of mint.

Almond tuiles

These crisp, thin biscuits are curved and take their name (which means tiles) from the terracotta roof pantiles much used round the Mediterranean. Bake the biscuits in batches, so the first lot can set while the other is in the oven. If you are short of rolling pins, improvise with milk bottles.

**Slimmer's portion, 1 biscuit:
Calories: 25
Carbohydrate units: ½**

MAKES ABOUT 48
2 small egg whites
40 g [1½ oz] plain flour
75 g [3 oz] caster sugar
40 g [1½ oz] nibbed almonds
40 g [1½ oz] butter, melted

1 Heat the oven to 190°C [375°F] gas mark 5. Lightly oil two or three rolling pins. Grease and line two large baking sheets with non-stick silicone paper.

2 Whisk the egg whites in a clean, dry bowl until stiff. Sift the flour over the whisked whites and fold in with a metal spoon.

3 Fold in the sugar and almonds, followed by the melted butter.

4 Using a 5 ml spoon [teaspoon], drop spoonfuls of the mixture on to each tray, spacing them well apart. Using the back of the spoon, smooth out into thin rounds.

5 Bake one tray at a time in the centre of the oven for 6–7 minutes until golden brown.

6 Using a palette knife, quickly, but carefully, remove the baked biscuits from the tray. Place over the oiled rolling pins so that the biscuits set in a curled shape. When set, slide off and allow to cool completely on a wire rack.

TREATS

Slimmers long for forbidden foods but it is most often those who try to stick too rigidly to a spartan regime who end up succumbing to temptation and putting on weight all over again. The trick is to allow yourself the right sort of treat occasionally. Here are some cakes and creamy desserts which won't wreck your diet but will help you to feel deliciously indulgent!

Light delights

Cakes, as a rule are well outside the limits (but not the dreams) of slimmers. However, there are occasions —a youngster's tea party perhaps or a coffee morning, when you want to treat yourself and others.

The answer is a delicious, classic whisked sponge. Made without fat and only a low proportion of flour, a whisked sponge cake is relatively low in Calories and carbohydrates when compared with other cakes.

Eat it the day of baking—on its own or served with fruit or topped with a fruit purée.

Fatless whisked sponge

The basic mix given here produces a light and airy sponge.

Slimmer's portion:
  Calories: 100
  Carbohydrate units: 3½

SERVES 6
50 g [2 oz] plain flour
2 large eggs
50 g [2 oz] caster sugar

1 Lightly grease and line a deep round 18 cm [7"] cake tin. Heat the oven to 180°C [350°F] gas mark 4.

2 Half fill a large saucepan with water. Bring to the boil, then remove from heat.

3 Sift the flour, twice, then put to one side. Break the eggs into a large mixing bowl and whisk lightly together. Add the sugar to the eggs and place the bowl over the pan of hot water. The bottom of the bowl must not touch the water.

4 Whisk the eggs and sugar together, using a balloon, rotary or electric whisk, until very light and creamy—the mixture should be thick enough to retain the impression of the whisk for three seconds.

David Levin

5 Remove the bowl from the pan and continue whisking until the mixture is cool and pale in colour.

6 Very lightly and gently fold in the sifted flour.

7 Pour the mixture into the tin and bake in the centre of the oven for about 45 minutes until the cake is firm to the touch and just shrinking from the sides of the tin.

8 Remove the baked cake from the oven, leave to stand for 30 seconds only then turn on to a wire cooling rack and strip off the lining paper. Turn the cake right side up and leave until quite cold.

Flavour variations

● Add 2–3 drops vanilla extract or 2.5 ml [½ teaspoon] finely grated orange or lemon zest to the eggs and sugar before whisking. (Calorie and carbohydrate units as basic mix.)

● Replace 15 g [½ oz] of the flour with an equal quantity of cocoa powder. Sift the cocoa with the flour.
Calories: 105
Carbohydrate units: 3½

● Replace 15 g [½ oz] of the flour with an equal quantity of fine, instant powdered coffee. Sift the coffee together with the flour.
Calories: 90
Carbohydrate units: 3

Cup cakes

These melt-in-the-mouth little cakes will be popular with all the family.

Slimmer's portion per cake:
Calories: 65
Carbohydrate units: 1½

MAKES 14 SMALL CAKES
basic sponge mix (page 52)
3½ glacé cherries
60 ml [4 tablespoons] thick cream

1 Arrange 14 paper cake cases on a baking tray, then heat the oven to 190°C [375°F] gas mark 5.

2 Make the basic mix and divide equally between the paper cases. Bake immediately in the centre of the oven for 12–15 minutes until they are well risen and firm to the touch.

3 Remove the baked cakes from the oven. Transfer the cakes to a wire rack and leave until completely cold.

4 Rinse the glacé cherries to remove excess syrup, then pat dry on kitchen paper. Cut each one into quarters.

5 Whisk the cream until thick, then place in a piping bag fitted with a star nozzle.

6 Pipe a whirl of cream in the centre of each cake and top with a piece of glacé cherry.

Strawberry sponge sandwich cake

Even slimmers can treat themselves to a generous portion of this cake. The strawberry-flavoured filling is fresh and creamy and low in Calories.
You will need 225 g [½ lb] strawberries to make 150 ml [¼ pt] purée.

Slimmer's portion:
Calories: 130
Carbohydrate units: 4½

SERVES 6
basic sponge mix (page 52)
150 ml [¼ pt] low-fat natural yoghurt
150 ml [¼ pt] strawberry purée
a few drops of artificial liquid sweetener
10 ml [2 teaspoons] gelatine
15 ml [1 tablespoon] caster sugar

1 Prepare and bake the basic sponge mix (see page 52).

2 Remove the baked cake from the oven and leave to stand for 30 seconds only, then turn out on to a wire cooling rack and strip off the lining paper. Turn the cake right side up and leave until quite cold.

3 In the meantime, prepare the filling. Stir the yoghurt into the strawberry purée until evenly blended.

4 Place the gelatine in a small, heavy-based pan with 30 ml [2 tablespoons] cold water. Leave for 4–5 minutes to soak. Then heat very gently until dissolved.

5 Pour the gelatine in a thin stream into the flavoured yoghurt, stirring constantly. Leave in a cool place until just on the point of setting. Stir occasionally to aid even setting. Add artificial liquid sweetener to taste, then set aside.

6 Cut the cold cake horizontally, into two equal layers. Place the bottom layer on a serving plate. Spread the almost-set jellied mixture carefully over the cake. Leave in a cool place for a few minutes to firm, then place the remaining layer of cake gently on top. Dredge the top of the cake with caster sugar.

Variation

● Whip 45 ml [3 tablespoons] thick cream until it will just hold its shape. Flavour with 1–2 drops almond essence, then fold in one skinned, stoned and finely chopped ripe peach. Whisk 1 medium-sized egg white until stiff, and then fold into the cream. Use to fill the cake.
Calories: 140
Carbohydrate units: 4

Forbidden fruits

Sugar, honey and other sweeteners are no longer the rare and precious commodities they once were. Unfortunately our modern habit is all too often to use such sweeteners indiscriminately and in excess—so that they mask rather than enhance the natural flavour of food.

If you are on a serious slimming campaign then sugar and syrups are just the sorts of things you should avoid—they contribute nothing in terms of food value and contain lots of Calories and carbohydrates you could well do without. If you think a little sugar won't hurt, try putting aside, in a bowl or jar, a duplicate of every single spoonful of sugar you use in the course of one day. You will be surprised at just how quickly it mounts up. Weigh the sugar you have set aside and multiply each 25 g [1 oz] by 110 Calories or 6 carbohydrate units. The total may well be enough to convince you that sugar is definitely out!

Cutting sugar out of your life can be a difficult job—particularly if you have a sweet tooth! The best plan is to reduce the amount you use gradually. This way you will become accustomed to a less sweet taste and in the process discover and enjoy the natural sweetness in food.

Artificial sweeteners

If you find the thought of life without sugar unpalatable, then artificial sweeteners can be a help. These are saccharin-based and their Calorie and carbohydrate content are negligible.

Artificial sweeteners are available in liquid, granular and tablet form. As a guide, one drop of liquid artificial sweetener is equivalent to a small lump of sugar and 6–8 drops are sufficient to sweeten 275 ml [½ pt] liquid, or 225 g [½ lb] stewed fruit.

Artificial sweeteners do have a synthetic edge to their taste and this is not improved if they are added to hot food. Also, if used in excess, the taste can be cloying. You can judge the amount required more accurately when the food is cold.

Although they are a sweetening agent, artificial sweeteners are not made of sugar and do not behave quite the same way in cooking. Always check the manufacturer's instructions for use in cooking.

Fruit

Fresh fruit is an excellent snack food as it is filling and refreshing without being fattening. It is, of course, also the ideal way to round off a meal. Take advantage of the summer abundance of soft fruit to make delicious fruit salads. There's no need to sweeten as the fruit contains plenty of natural sugar; simply turn the fruit in freshly suqeezed orange juice (this provides extra juice and also helps bring out the flavour of the fruit). Low-carbohydrate slimmers top their portion of fruit salad with a dollop of cream while those on a low-Calorie diet should go for creamy low-fat natural yoghurt.

Canned fruit is a useful store-cupboard item. Avoid fruit canned in syrup and choose instead fruit canned in its natural juice.

Dried fruit, as its name implies, contains less water than fresh or canned fruit and therefore contains, weight for weight, more Calories or carbohydrate units. However, when dried fruit is soaked and reconstituted, it becomes equal to fresh fruit in Calories and carbohydrate units.

Desserts

Delicious as it is, fresh fruit can pall. Luckily, a great many suitably 'slimming' fluffy fruit desserts can be made based on fruit juices and purées, whipped egg whites and yoghurt. Sometimes gelatine is used to stabilize and set the mixture. (See apricot mousse on page 56 or creamy yoghurt jelly on page 57.)

If you fancy a treat that is quick to make, try any of the following (quantities are enough for two).
● For fruity yoghurt fluff, whisk one medium-sized egg white until stiff, then fold into 125 ml [4 fl oz] low-fat natural yoghurt. Add 15 ml [1 tablespoon] unsweetened fruit purée and fold in to give a marbled effect (Calories: 115; Carbohydrate units: 2).
● For slimmers' summer fool, beat 30 ml [2 tablespoons] low-fat natural yoghurt together with 50 g [2 oz] sieved cottage cheese until smooth. Blend in 75 ml [3 fl oz] thick, unsweetened fruit purée. Sweeten to taste with liquid artificial sweetener. Chill in refrigerator 15 minutes (Calories: 120; carbohydrate units: 2).
● To make a yoghurt foam, simply fold into one medium-sized, stiffly beaten egg white 125 ml [4 fl oz] of fruit-flavoured yoghurt (Calories: 140; carbohydrate units: ½).

Star recipe

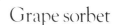

Grape sorbet

Made the traditional way, with sugar syrup, sorbets are not for slimmers. Here is a version low enough in carbohydrates and Calories that the slimmer can share with the family or friends. It can be made with red grape juice and garnished with black grapes, or white grape juice and decorated with green grapes. Be sure to buy real grape juice for this recipe and not 'grape juice drink'. Check that the sorbet container will fit in the ice compartment of your refrigerator. Serve the sorbet on the day of making.

Slimmer's portion:
Calories: 70
Carbohydrate units: 4

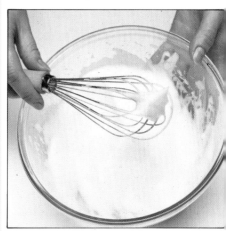

3 Put the egg whites in a spotlessly clean, dry bowl and whisk until fluffy and standing in soft peaks. Next, using a fork, break up the grape juice ice.

SERVES 4
275 ml [½ pt] grape juice
25 g [1 oz] caster sugar
2 medium-sized egg whites
15 ml [1 tablespoon] lemon juice

1 Adjust the refrigerator to its maximum coldest setting. Pour all of the grape juice into a bowl, then add the caster sugar and stir very well.

2 Pour the mixture into a shallow polythene container and place in the freezer compartment; leave for about 1 hour or until frozen 2.5 cm [1"] all round the edges.

4 Add the ice gradually to the egg whites, whisking continuously. Add the lemon juice and continue whisking until the mixture is very light and bulky.

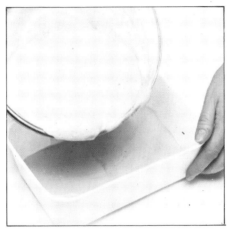

5 Return the mixture to the container. Place in the freezer compartment of the refrigerator and leave for about 1 hour until it becomes thoroughly frozen.

6 To serve, divide mixture between four glass dishes. Cut each grape in half and remove the pips, then decorate each serving with two grapes.

Apricot mousse

⊠⊠⊠ *Dried apricots are useful in a slimming diet because they provide a natural source of sugar without being too fattening. They are also very nourishing, being packed with iron as well as vitamin A. Serve them on their own, with yoghurt to make a simple fool, chopped into salads or, for something a little more elaborate, try this mousse.*

Slimmer's portion:
Calories: 115
Carbohydrate units: 5

SERVES 4
225 g [½ lb] dried apricots
15 g [½ oz] gelatine
5 ml [1 teaspoon] shredded orange zest, blanched
2 medium-sized egg whites

To serve:
a little shredded orange zest, blanched

1 Cover the apricots with boiling water and leave to soak for 8 hours or overnight. Drain. Reserve the liquid and make up to 150 ml [¼ pt] if necessary with fresh orange juice.

2 Put 45 ml [3 tablespoons] cold water into a heavy-based saucepan and sprinkle over the gelatine. Leave to soak for 5 minutes, then dissolve for 3 minutes over low heat without stirring. Remove from the heat; set aside and allow to cool.

3 In the meantime, put the apricots, reserved liquid and orange zest in a liquidizer, and blend until smooth. Pour the purée into a bowl.

4 As soon as the gelatine has cooled, pour it into the apricot purée in a thin stream, stirring constantly.

5 Put the egg white in a spotlessly clean, dry bowl and whisk until stiff but not dry. Then fold into the apricot mixture using a metal spoon.

6 Spoon the mixture into 4 glass serving dishes and leave about 1 hour until set. To serve, decorate the surface of each portion with a sprinkling of the shredded orange zest.

Variation
● For prune whip, soak the prunes in hot tea with slices of lemon. Simmer them in this liquid. Remove stones. Substitute lemon zest for the orange and finish in the same way as the apricot mousse.
Calories: 105
Carbohydrate units: 4

Strawberry delight

⊠ *Strawberries coated with creamy low-fat natural yoghurt and topped with crunchy Demarara sugar make a luxurious dessert that doesn't seem at all like slimmers' fare! Yet at about 110 Calories or 5 carbohydrate units a serving, this sweet will fit into most diets to give slimmers the treat they deserve for all the will-power they demonstrate.*

Slimmer's portion:
Calories: 115
Carbohydrate units: 5

SERVES 4
350 g [¾ lb] fresh strawberries
225 ml [8 fl oz] low-fat natural yoghurt
50 g [2 oz] Demerara sugar

1 Rinse then hull the strawberries; halve or quarter any very large ones.

2 Put the strawberries into a shallow glass serving dish.

3 Pour the yoghurt over the strawberries. Chill in the refrigerator for at least half an hour.

4 Just before serving, sprinkle the sugar evenly over the top.

Variations
● For raspberry delight, use fresh raspberries instead of strawberries.
Calories: 115
Carbohydrate units: 5
● For grape delight, use black grapes instead of strawberries. Halve the grapes and remove the pips. Stir in the yoghurt with soft brown sugar instead of sprinkling Demerara on top.
Calories: 145
Carbohydrate units: 6

Real pineapple jelly

⊠⊠ *Making your own jelly with fruit juice is deliciously refreshing as well as being lower in Calories and carbohydrates than the bought cubes. They are nutritious, too and need not be served only as desserts. They make very nice accompaniments to cottage cheese on a bed of lettuce for a complete salad light meal. Different fruit juices can be used for variety and for a change of texture, yoghurt or whisked egg white can also be added.*

Slimmer's portion:
Calories: 110
Carbohydrate units: 4½

SERVES 4
15 g [½ oz] gelatine
575 ml [1 pt] canned unsweetened pineapple juice
zest of 1 orange

To serve:
75 g [3 oz] canned or fresh pineapple chunks
60 ml [4 tablespoons] low-fat natural yoghurt

1 Put 45 ml [3 tablespoons] cold water into a heavy-based saucepan and sprinkle over the gelatine. Leave to soak for 5 minutes, then dissolve for 3 minutes over low heat, without stirring. Remove from the heat to allow to cool.

2 Pour the pineapple juice into a large bowl and add the orange zest. As soon as the gelatine has cooled, pour it into the pineapple juice in a thin stream, stirring continuously.

3 Pour the jelly into four individual glass dishes and chill in the refrigerator for 1–2 hours until set.

4 Decorate each with pineapple chunks and a blob of yoghurt.

Variations
● For orange fruit jelly, use fresh orange juice and flavour with lemon zest. Arrange a couple of grapes cut in half with pips removed and slices of one red-skinned apple in each dish before pouring in the jelly. Turn out to serve.
Calories: 90
Carbohydrate units: 3½
● To make a lighter textured jelly

fluff, add the lightly whisked white of a medium-sized egg to the jelly when it is just on the point of setting. Then divide between dishes and leave to set completely.
Depending on the fruit juice used:
    Calories: 60–90
    Carbohydrate units: 2–4

● For creamy yoghurt jelly, use only 425 ml [¾ pt] fruit juice and whisk in 150 ml [¼ pt] low-fat natural yoghurt before adding the gelatine.
Depending on the fruit juice used:
    Calories: 65–85
    Carbohydrate units: 2–3
● For tomato mould, use tomato juice, flavour with Worcestershire sauce, onion and lemon juice, salt and pepper. Decorate with cucumber slivers. This makes a tasty alternative when salad tomatoes are not at their best. Garnish with watercress.
    Calories: 30
    Carbohydrate units: 1

Life savers

Anyone who has ever tried to diet will know the value of a soothing drink to help them over those low energy periods. When a 'low' hits, don't automatically reach for the biscuit tin. Make a drink instead, take it out of the kitchen and drink it slowly, preferably with your feet up and something interesting to read. Black coffee and tea (including fragrant jasmine tea and herbal teas) are the drinks to choose when you want slimming refreshment. The homemade slimmer's lemonade (see page 60) is also useful.

Beverages also have a place in a slimming diet as replacement meals; these are usually based on a protein ingredient such as egg, buttermilk, yoghurt or skimmed milk. A liquidizer is essential for making them. When adapting a recipe, replace any sugar or honey in the ingredients with artificial liquid sweetener.

Fresh vegetable cocktail

It is important to remove the seeds from the tomatoes for this drink, otherwise they would give a bitter flavour.

> **Slimmer's serving, 150 ml**
> **[¼ pt]:**
>   **Calories: 15**
>   **Carbohydrate units: 1**
> MAKES ABOUT 1.2 L [2¼ PT]
> **450 g [1 lb] tomatoes**
> **1 large carrot**
> **2 celery sticks**
> **half a bunch of watercress**
> **5 ml [1 teaspoon] yeast**
>   **extract**
> **275 ml [½ pt] tomato juice**
> **celery salt**
> **freshly ground black pepper**

1 Skin, halve and de-seed the tomatoes. Grate the carrot and chop the celery. Strip the leaves from the watercress, discarding the stalks and any yellowing leaves.

2 Dissolve the yeast extract in 425 ml [¾ pt] warm water. Put in a liquidizer with the tomato juice, tomatoes, carrots, celery and watercress leaves. Blend.

3 Check seasoning and refrigerate for 2 hours before serving.

Alcoholic drinks can ruin any diet—if you are giving a party, here are two sensible suggestions:

Sparkling cider cup

Surprisingly enough, cider is relatively low in Calories. Here, it is mixed with some sparkling soda water and flavoured with brandy, orange, lemon and cucumber to make a refreshing party drink that will not destroy your diet.

> **Slimmer's serving, 150 ml**
> **[¼ pt] with dry cider:**
>   **Calories: 60**
>   **Carbohydrate units: 2**
> **Slimmer's serving, 150 ml**
> **[¼ pt] with sweet cider:**
>   **Calories: 75**
>   **Carbohydrate units: 2½**
>
> MAKES ABOUT 1.4 L [2½ PT]
> **1 L [1¾ pt] sweet or dry cider**
> **thinly pared rind of 1 large**
>   **orange**
> **thinly pared rind of 1 large**
>   **lemon**
> **thinly peeled skin from half a**
>   **cucumber**
> **75 ml [3 fl oz] brandy**
> **400 ml [14 fl oz] soda water**

1 Put the orange and lemon rind in a large bowl or jug, together with cucumber skin. Pour in the brandy.

2 Using a spoon, bruise the skin and rinds slightly to extract flavour. Cover and leave 1–2 hours.

3 Add the cider to the brandy mixture. Just before serving mix in the soda water.

Sangria

This is a very popular—and very inexpensive—summer drink. Because the wine is 'thinned' with soda water, the Calorie or carbohydrate units per glassful are reasonably low.

> **Slimmer's serving, 150 ml**
> **[¼ pt]:**
>   **Calories: 80**
>   **Carbohydrate units: 4**
>
> MAKES ABOUT 1 L [1¾ PT]
> **1 medium-sized orange**
> **1 medium-sized lemon**
> **700 ml [25 fl oz] dry red wine**
> **275 ml [½ pt] soda water**

1 Wash the orange and lemon. Thinly pare the peel from the fruit, keeping it in fairly long strips. Put the peel into a punch bowl.

2 Using a sharp knife, cut away all the white pith from the fruit. Next, cut the flesh into segments. Remove any pips, then cut the segments in half.

3 Add the segments to the peel, then pour over the wine. Chill in the refrigerator for at least one hour.

4 Just before serving, stir in the soda water.

Slimmer's lemonade

☒ *This lemonade is easy to make with the aid of a liquidizer and is wonderfully refreshing on a hot summer day. The lemonade can be diluted with a little more cold water if liked.*

Slimmer's serving, 275 ml [½ pt]:
Calories: negligible
Carbohydrate units: ½

MAKES ABOUT 1.4 L [2½ PT]
2 lemons
liquid artificial sweetener to taste

1 Wash the lemons, then slice roughly.

2 Put the lemon slices, 12 ice cubes and 1.1 L [2 pt] water into a liquidizer. Blend at high speed for 10 seconds. (Be careful not to over-blend as this can result in a bitter taste.)

3 Strain the lemonade into a jug and sweeten to taste with liquid artificial sweetener. Refrigerate until required.

Iced tea

☒☒☒ *China tea is always preferable for this recipe as Indian tea becomes rather bitter when allowed to stand. Iced tea is equally delicious made with herbal tea.*

Slimmer's serving, 275 ml [½ pt]:
Calories: 15
Carbohydrate units: 1

MAKES ABOUT 1.1 L [2 PT]
15 ml [1 tablespoon] tea
1 orange
1 lemon
a few sprigs of mint

1 Wash the orange and the lemon. Finely pare the rind from half the orange and half the lemon, taking care not to pare the white pith. Reserve the rind.

2 Squeeze the juices from the fruit and pour into a 1.1 L [2 pt] glass jug. Add the orange and lemon rinds.

3 Put the tea in a large bowl and pour over 225 ml [8 fl oz] boiling water. Allow to infuse for 10 minutes then strain on to the fruit juices and rinds.

4 Add 900 ml [32 fl oz] cold water and stir well. Add the mint and refrigerate overnight.

Raspberry milk-shake

☒ *This is a filling drink which can make a complete light meal in itself. Make sure the yoghurt and water are well chilled so that the drink is refreshingly cold, or use a little less water and add two or three ice cubes. Sip this through a straw to make it last longer!*

Milk shakes of other flavours can be made by varying the type of yoghurt used: strawberry, pineapple, mandarin and blackcurrant are all good flavours to use.

Calories: 170
Carbohydrate units: 2

SERVES 1
125 ml [4 fl oz] low-fat raspberry yoghurt
15 g [½ oz] skimmed milk powder

1 Put the ingredients into a liquidizer with 150 ml [¼ pt] chilled water and blend at high speed until smooth and creamy.

2 Pour into a tall glass and serve immediately.

In the foreground: orange and egg reviver, left, and iced tea. Behind: slimmer's lemonade, left, and raspberry milk-shake.

Orange and egg reviver

☒ *This is a protein-rich drink full of vitamin C that is excellent for filling an energy gap. Measure the honey carefully (30 Calories or ½ carbohydrate unit per 5 ml [1 teaspoon]) otherwise it will not be so slimming after all!*

Calories: 140
Carbohydrate units: 2½

SERVES 1
1 large orange
1 medium-sized egg
5 ml [1 teaspoon] thin honey
few drops of artificial sweetener

1 Grate the zest from half the orange, then peel whole orange. Chop flesh roughly and put both zest and flesh into a liquidizer; break in egg, then add 150 ml [¼ pt] water, honey and artificial sweetener.

2 Blend at high speed for 1–2 minutes until fairly smooth.

3 Pour into a glass and serve with a long spoon to scoop up the pulp.

CALORIE AND CARBOHYDRATE CHART

BREAD, CEREALS ETC

	Weight	Cals	CU		Weight	Cals	CU
Barley, raw	25 g [1 oz]	100	5	Mozzarella	25 g [1 oz]	100	0
boiled	25 g [1 oz]	35	1½	Parmesan	15 ml [1 tbs]	30	0
Biscuits				Roquefort	25 g [1 oz]	90	0
cream cracker	one	40	1	White Stilton	25 g [1 oz]	95	0
digestive	one	60	2	**Cream**			
ginger	one	40	1	clotted	15 ml [1 tbs]	105	0
Bread				thick	15 ml [1 tbs]	60	0
bap	50 g [2 oz]	120	5	thin	15 ml [1 tbs]	30	0
croissant	50 g [2 oz]	270	4	soured	15 ml [1 tbs]	25	0
crumbs	15 ml [1 tbs]	30	1½	whipping	15 ml [1 tbs]	65	0
crumpet, no butter	40 g [1½ oz]	75	3	**Dripping/lard**	25 g [1 oz]	250	0
crusty roll	50 g [2 oz]	145	4½	**Egg,** boiled,			
French bread	50 g [2 oz]	130	6	poached or raw	one large	95	0
white, large loaf	40 g [1½ oz] slice	100	4½	fried	one large	145	0
white, small loaf	25 g [1 oz] slice	65	3	yolk	one medium	60	0
wholemeal, small	25 g [1 oz] slice	60	2½	white	one medium	15	0
pitta	40 g [1½ oz]	125	5	**Margarine**			
Breakfast cereals				hard or soft	15 g [½ oz]	100	0
bran type	25 g [1 oz]	70	3½	**Milk,** buttermilk	575 ml [1 pt]	200	5½
cornflakes	25 g [1 oz]	100	5	high cream	575 ml [1 pt]	430	5½
muesli type	25 g [1 oz]	105	4	goat's	575 ml [1 pt]	400	5½
porridge	25 g [1 oz]	105	4	longlife	575 ml [1 pt]	370	5½
Cornflour	25 g [1 oz]	100	5	low-fat	575 ml [1 pt]	200	5½
Crispbread, average	one	30	1	pasteurized	575 ml [1 pt]	370	5½
Flour				powdered dry	25 g [1 oz]	90	2½
plain white	25 g [1 oz]	100	4½	skimmed	575 ml [1 pt]	200	5½
self-raising	25 g [1 oz]	95	4½	sterilized	575 ml [1 pt]	370	5½
wheatmeal	25 g [1 oz]	95	4½	canned:			
wholemeal	25 g [1 oz]	80	4	evaporated	25 g [1 oz]	45	½
Macaroni, raw	25 g [1 oz]	105	4½	condensed	25 g [1 oz]	90	3
boiled	25 g [1 oz]	35	1½	**Oils**			
Noodles, boiled	25 g [1 oz]	35	1	nut	15 ml [1 tbs]	140	neg
Pastry				olive	15 ml [1 tbs]	120	0
shortcrust, baked	25 g [1 oz]	150	3	sunflower seed	15 ml [1 tbs]	120	neg
flaky or puff, baked	25 g [1 oz]	160	3	vegetable	15 ml [1 tbs]	120	0
Rice, raw	25 g [1 oz]	100	5	**Suet**	25 g [1 oz]	235	1½
boiled	25 g [1 oz]	35	2	**Yoghurt**			
Spaghetti, raw	25 g [1 oz]	105	5	low-fat natural	125 ml [4 fl oz]	85	½
boiled	25 g [1 oz]	35	1½	fruit, sweetened	125 ml [4 fl oz]	125	½
Wheatgerm	25 g [1 oz]	100	3	hazelnut	125 ml [4 fl oz]	150	1

DAIRY PRODUCE, FATS AND OILS

DRINKS

	Weight	Cals	CU		Weight	Cals	CU
				Aperitifs			
Butter	15 g [½ oz]	105	0	Campari	25 ml [1 fl oz]	70	3½
Cheese				Dubonnet, red	25 ml [1 fl oz]	45	2½
Blue Stilton	25 g [1 oz]	130	0	Sherry, dry	25 ml [1 fl oz]	30	1½
Brie	25 g [1 oz]	90	0	Sherry, medium	25 ml [1 fl oz]	35	1½
Caerphilly	25 g [1 oz]	120	0	Sherry, cream	25 ml [1 fl oz]	40	2
Camembert	25 g [1 oz]	90	0	Vermouth, bianco	25 ml [1 fl oz]	45	2½
Cheddar	25 g [1 oz]	120	0	Vermouth, red	25 ml [1 fl oz]	45	2½
Cheshire	25 g [1 oz]	110	0	Vermouth, dry	25 ml [1 fl oz]	35	1½
Cottage	25 g [1 oz]	25	0	**Beer,** bitter	575 ml [1 pt]	190	10
Cream	25 g [1 oz]	125	0	barley wine	275 ml [½ pt]	255	13½
Curd	25 g [1 oz]	40	0	brown	575 ml [1 pt]	185	9½
Danish Blue	25 g [1 oz]	105	0	lager	575 ml [1 pt]	170	9
Edam	25 g [1 oz]	90	0	low-calorie lager	275 ml [½ pt]	80	4
Gorgonzola	25 g [1 oz]	110	0	pale	575 ml [1 pt]	170	9
Gruyère	25 g [1 oz]	130	0	shandy	575 ml [1 pt]	135	7
Leicester	25 g [1 oz]	105	0	stout	575 ml [1 pt]	225	12

	Weight	Cals	CU
strong bitter	575 ml [1 pt]	340	18
Cider, dry	575 ml [1 pt]	225	12
medium	575 ml [1 pt]	170	9
special dry	575 ml [1 pt]	265	14
Liqueurs, Advocaat	25 ml [1 fl oz]	70	$3\frac{1}{2}$
Benedictine	25 ml [1 fl oz]	110	$5\frac{1}{2}$
Calvados	25 ml [1 fl oz]	75	$3\frac{1}{2}$
Chartreuse	25 ml [1 fl oz]	120	6
Cherry brandy	25 ml [1 fl oz]	80	4
Cointreau	25 ml [1 fl oz]	100	5
Crème de menthe	25 ml [1 fl oz]	95	5
Grand Marnier	25 ml [1 fl oz]	95	$4\frac{1}{2}$
Mixer drinks, tonic	125 ml [4 fl oz]	30	$1\frac{1}{2}$
low-calorie tonic	125 ml [4 fl oz]	0	0
ginger ale	125 ml [4 fl oz]	40	$1\frac{1}{2}$
low-calorie ginger ale	125 ml [4 fl oz]	0	0
lemonade	125 ml [4 fl oz]	30	2
bitter lemon	125 ml [4 fl oz]	40	2
Spirits, gin, rum, vodka, whisky	25 ml [1 fl oz]	60	3
Wines, dry white	125 ml [4 fl oz]	75	4
sparkling white	125 ml [4 fl oz]	90	$4\frac{1}{2}$
sweet white	125 ml [4 fl oz]	100	5
dry red, rosé	125 ml [4 fl oz]	80	4
sweet red	125 ml [4 fl oz]	95	5
ginger wine	125 ml [4 fl oz]	230	$11\frac{1}{2}$
port	25 ml [1 fl oz]	45	$2\frac{1}{2}$

Coffee and **tea** are nil.

FRUIT

	Weight	Cals	CU
Apples, dessert	one, 100 g [$\frac{1}{4}$ lb]	40	2
juice	125 ml [4 fl oz]	40	2
Apricots, fresh	one medium	5	$\frac{1}{2}$
canned	25 g [1 oz]	30	$1\frac{1}{2}$
dried	25 g [1 oz]	50	$2\frac{1}{2}$
Banana, whole	one medium	80	4
Blackberries, fresh	25 g [1 oz]	10	$\frac{1}{2}$
Blackcurrants, fresh	25 g [1 oz]	10	$\frac{1}{2}$
Cherries, glacé	one medium	10	$\frac{1}{2}$
fresh, unstoned	25 g [1 oz]	10	$\frac{1}{2}$
canned in syrup	100 g [$\frac{1}{4}$ lb]	95	$4\frac{1}{2}$
Cranberry sauce	25 g [1 oz]	45	1
Currants	25 g [1 oz]	70	$3\frac{1}{2}$
Damsons fresh, stoned	25 g [1 oz]	10	$\frac{1}{2}$
Dates, unstoned	25 g [1 oz]	60	4
Figs, green	25 g [1 oz]	10	$\frac{1}{2}$
dried	one medium	30	$1\frac{1}{2}$
Gooseberries			
dessert, fresh	25 g [1 oz]	10	$\frac{1}{2}$
cooking, fresh	25 g [1 oz]	5	neg
Grapefruit, fresh	medium, half	15	neg
canned in syrup	25 g [1 oz]	15	1
juice	125 ml [4 fl oz]	40	2
Grapes, black/white	25 g [1 oz]	15	1
juice	125 ml [4 fl oz]	60	4
Greengages			
fresh, unstoned	25 g [1 oz]	15	1
Lemons, fresh	one medium	20	1
juice	15 ml [1 tbs]	0	neg
Lychees, flesh only	25 g [1 oz]	20	1

	Weight	Cals	CU
Mandarins, fresh	one medium	20	$\frac{1}{2}$
canned	25 g [1 oz]	15	1
Mango, fresh	25 g [1 oz]	15	1
Melons, Cantaloup. Honeydew, Ogen	100 g [$\frac{1}{4}$ lb] slice	50	$\frac{1}{2}$
Watermelon	100 g [$\frac{1}{4}$ lb] slice	20	$\frac{1}{2}$
Nectarines	25 g [1 oz]	15	1
Oranges, fresh	one medium	35	2
juice	125 ml [4 fl oz]	50	3
Peaches, fresh	one medium	35	2
canned, drained	one half	25	1
Pears, fresh	one medium	35	2
canned, drained	one half	30	$1\frac{1}{2}$
Pineapple, fresh	25 g [1 oz]	15	1
canned, drained	one ring	35	$1\frac{1}{2}$
juice	125 ml [4 fl oz]	60	3
Plums			
dessert, fresh	one medium	15	$\frac{1}{2}$
Prunes, dried	25 g [1 oz]	45	2
stewed, no sugar	25 g [1 oz]	25	1
Raisins	25 g [1 oz]	70	4
	15 ml [1 tbs]	25	3
Raspberries, fresh	25 g [1 oz]	5	$\frac{1}{2}$
canned, drained	25 g [1 oz]	25	$1\frac{1}{2}$
Rhubarb	one stick	5	neg
Strawberries, fresh	25 g [1 oz]	5	$\frac{1}{2}$
canned, drained	25 g [1 oz]	25	1
Sultanas	25 g [1 oz]	70	4
Tangerines, fresh	one medium	20	1

MEAT AND FISH

	Weight	Cals	CU
Anchovy	one medium	5	neg
paste	5 ml [1 tsp]	5	neg
Bacon			
grilled or fried back	medium rasher	80	0
grilled or fried streaky	medium rasher	50	0
Beef			
minced, drained of fat	100 g [$\frac{1}{4}$ lb]	220	0
silverside, boiled	100 g [$\frac{1}{4}$ lb]	360	0
stewing steak, raw	100 g [$\frac{1}{4}$ lb]	200	0
steak, grilled	225 g [$\frac{1}{2}$ lb]	370	0
steak, fried	225 g [$\frac{1}{2}$ lb]	440	0
Brains, raw	100 g [$\frac{1}{4}$ lb]	120	0
Chicken			
on bone, baked	275 g [10 oz] raw	250	0
drumstick, grilled	125 g [$\frac{1}{4}$ lb] raw	90	0
drumstick, fried	125 g [$\frac{1}{4}$ lb] raw	110	0
Cod			
fillet, steamed	175 g [6 oz]	150	0
fried in batter	175 g [6 oz] raw	330	$4\frac{1}{2}$
roe, fried	25 g [1 oz]	55	0
Coley			
fillet, steamed	175 g [6 oz]	180	0
Corned beef	25 g [1 oz]	60	0
Crab meat, boiled	25 g [1 oz]	35	0
Eel, jellied	75 g [3 oz]	320	neg

	Weight	Cals	CU
Haddock			
smoked fillet, steamed or poached	100 g [¼ lb]	120	0
fillet, fried: in batter	175 g [6 oz] raw	460	4½
in crumbs	175 g [6 oz] raw	435	4½
Hake			
fillet, steamed	175 g [6 oz]	180	0
Ham, lean, boiled	100 g [¼ lb]	240	0
steak, well grilled	200 g [7 oz]	270	0
Heart, lamb's, raw	100 g [¼ lb]	140	0
Herring			
whole, grilled	150 g [5 oz]	200	0
on bone, fried in oatmeal	150 g [5 oz]	300	4
roe, fried	25 g [1 oz]	70	0
Kidney, all kinds, raw	25 g [1 oz]	25	0
lamb's, grilled	one medium	50	0
lamb's, fried	one medium	65	0
Kipper, whole, grilled	175 g [6 oz] raw	280	0
Lamb			
lean chump chop, well grilled	175 g [6 oz] raw	230	0
lean loin chop, well grilled	175 g [6 oz] raw	10	0
middle neck, stewed	175 g [6 oz]	510	0
Lemon sole, fillet, grilled or steamed	100 g [¼ lb]	100	0
Liver			
chicken, raw	25 g [1 oz]	40	0
lamb, raw	25 g [1 oz]	50	0
lamb, grilled	100 g [¼ lb]	200	0
pig, raw	25 g [1 oz]	45	0
Lobster meat, boiled	100 g [¼ lb]	140	0
Luncheon meat	25 g [1 oz]	90	½
Mackerel, smoked	25 g [1 oz]	70	0
on bone, fried	25 g [1 oz]	40	0
Mullet	100 g [¼ lb] raw	160	0
Mussels	25 g [1 oz]	25	0
Octopus	100 g [¼ lb] raw	80	0
Oysters, raw	one	5	0
Pâté, liver	25 g [1 oz]	80	neg
duck and orange	25 g [1 oz]	80	2
Pheasant			
on bone, roast	25 g [1 oz]	30	0
off bone, roast	25 g [1 oz]	60	0
Pigeon			
on bone, roast	25 g [1 oz]	30	0
off bone, roast	25 g [1 oz]	65	0
Pilchard, canned, in tomato sauce	25 g [1 oz]	35	0
Plaice			
fillet, steamed	175 g [6 oz]	150	0
fillet, fried in batter	175 g [6 oz]	480	0
fried in crumbs	175 g [6 oz]	390	4½
Pork, crackling	25 g [1 oz]	190	0
chop, well grilled	175 g [6 oz] raw	250	0
spare ribs	25 g [1 oz]	55	0

	Weight	Cals	CU
Prawns, boiled, shelled	25 g [1 oz]	30	0
Rabbit			
on bone, stewed	225 g [½ lb]	200	0
off bone, stewed	225 g [½ lb]	400	0
Salmon, canned	100 g [¼ lb]	180	0
on bone, steamed	100 g [¼ lb]	180	0
smoked	25 g [1 oz]	40	0
Sardine, canned:			
in tomato	one medium	50	0
in oil	one medium	60	0
Sausage			
pork, grilled	one medium	115	½
pork chipolata: well fried or grilled	one medium	65	½
frankfurter	one medium	80	neg
garlic sausage	25 g [1 oz]	70	neg
liver sausage	25 g [1 oz]	90	neg
salami, Danish	25 g [1 oz]	160	0
Scampi, fried in crumbs	25 g [1 oz]	90	1½
Shrimps			
with shells, boiled	25 g [1 oz]	10	0
shelled, raw	25 g [1 oz]	35	0
Skate, fillet, fried in batter	175 g [6 oz]	330	4½
Sole, on bone, steamed	175 g [6 oz]	120	0
Sweetbreads, fried	25 g [1 oz]	65	0
Tongue, ox	25 g [1 oz]	85	0
Tripe, stewed	25 g [1 oz]	30	0
Trout			
steamed	one medium	170	0
smoked	175 g [6 oz]	210	0
Tuna, canned, in oil	25 g [1 oz]	80	0
drained	25 g [1 oz]	60	0
Veal, fillet, roast	25 g [1 oz]	65	0
Whitebait, fried	25 g [1 oz]	150	0
Whiting on bone, steamed	175 g [6 oz]	120	0

(For general roast meat chart, see page 26.)

NUTS

	Weight	Cals	CU
Almonds, whole	one	10	neg
flakes	15 ml [1 tbs]	160	neg
ground	15 ml [1 tbs]	30	neg
Brazil nuts, whole	one	20	neg
Cashews, whole	one	15	1½
Chestnuts, shelled	25 g [1 oz]	50	2
Coconut, fresh	25 g [1 oz]	100	neg
desiccated	25 g [1 oz]	170	½
Hazelnuts, shelled	25 g [1 oz]	110	1
Peanuts, roasted	25 g [1 oz]	160	½
Pistachio nuts, shelled	25 g [1 oz]	180	neg
Walnuts, shelled	25 g [1 oz]	155	neg
chopped	15 ml [1 tbs]	50	neg

SAUCES AND FLAVOURINGS

	Weight	Cals	CU
Baking powder	5 ml [1 tsp]	5	neg
Black pepper, corns	30	5	0
ground	2.5 ml [½ tsp]	5	0
Capers	25 g [1 oz]	5	neg
Chives	25 g [1 oz]	10	neg
Curry, powder	5 ml [1 tsp]	10	neg
paste	25 g [1 oz]	45	neg
Garlic	one clove	0	neg
Gelatine	15 ml [1 tbs]	30	0
Gherkins	25 g [1 oz]	5	neg
Ginger, ground	5 ml [1 tsp]	10	neg
stem, in syrup	25 g [1 oz]	80	4
Gravy, thick	15 ml [1 tbs]	30	3
thin, no fat	15 ml [1 tbs]	5	neg
Horseradish sauce	15 [1 tbs]	15	½
Mango chutney	15 ml [1 tbs]	35	2
Mayonnaise	15 ml [1 tbs]	95	0
Mint, sauce	15 ml [1 tbs]	25	½
jelly	25 g [1 oz]	95	2
Mustard, made	15 ml [1 tbs]	30	neg
powder	25 g [1 oz]	130	neg
powder	5 ml [1 tsp]	20	neg
Salt	25 g [1 oz]	0	0
Sesame seeds	25 g [1 oz]	160	neg
Soy sauce	15 ml [1 tbs]	5	neg
Stock, skimmed of fat	425 ml [¾ pt]	30	neg
Vanilla extract	5 ml [1 tsp]	0	neg
Vinegar	15 ml [1 tbs]	0	neg
Worcestershire sauce	15 ml [1 tbs]	10	neg
Yeast, fresh	25 g [1 oz]	15	neg
dried	25 g [1 oz]	50	neg
extract	25 g [1 oz]	40	0

SWEET FOOD

	Weight	Cals	CU
Candied peel	15 ml [1 tbs]	45	3
Chocolate			
milk or plain	25 g [1 oz]	150	3½
cooking	25.5 g [1 oz]	155	3½
cocoa powder	15 ml [1 tbs]	15	neg
Custard powder	25 g [1 oz]	100	5
Honey	15 ml [1 tbs]	60	1½
Ice-cream	25 g [1 oz]	50	3½
Jam (all kinds)	5 ml [1 tsp]	15	1½
Jelly			
tablet form	25 g [1 oz]	75	5
made up with water	25 g [1 oz]	15	½
Lemon curd	15 ml [1 tbs]	45	3
Marzipan	25 g [1 oz]	125	3
Mincemeat	15 ml [1 tbs]	40	3½
Molasses	15 ml [1 tbs]	45	2
Sugar (all kinds)	25 g [1 oz]	110	6
	5 ml [1 tsp]	15	½
Sweets, boiled	25 g [1 oz]	95	5
fudge	25 g [1 oz]	110	4
toffee	25 g [1 oz]	120	4
Syrup, golden	15 ml [1 tbs]	85	4
Treacle	15 ml [1 tbs]	75	3½

VEGETABLES

	Weight	Cals	CU
Artichoke			
globe, cooked	225 g [8 oz]	15	neg
Jerusalem, boiled	25 g [1 oz]	5	neg
Asparagus	on spear	5	neg
Aubergine	200 g [7 oz]	30	neg
Avocado pear	medium-half	315	½
Beans, baked	25 g [1 oz]	20	1
broad, boiled	25 g [1 oz]	15	½
French, boiled	25 g [1 oz]	0	neg
kidney, canned	25 g [1 oz]	25	1
runner, boiled	25 g [1 oz]	5	neg
soya, raw	25 g [1 oz]	115	2
Beansprouts, raw	25 g [1 oz]	10	neg
Beetroot, boiled	25 g [1 oz]	15	½
pickled	15 ml [1 tbs]	10	½
Broccoli, boiled	25 g [1 oz]	5	neg
Brussels sprouts	one medium	5	neg
Cabbage	25 g [1 oz]	5	neg
Carrots	25 g [1 oz]	5	½
Cauliflower	25 g [1 oz]	5	neg
Celery, raw	one stick	5	neg
Courgettes	one medium	10	neg
Cucumber	25 g [1 oz]	5	neg
Leeks	25 g [1 oz]	10	½
Lentils, raw	25 g [1 oz]	85	3
boiled	25 g [1 oz]	30	1
Lettuce, whole	small	15	neg
Marrow, boiled	25 g [1 oz]	5	neg
Mushrooms, raw	25 g [1 oz]	0	neg
button, fried	25 g [1 oz] raw	40	neg
Olives, stuffed	one	5	neg
Onions, raw	25 g [1 oz]	5	½
fried	25 g [1 oz]	100	½
pickled	one	5	neg
dried flakes	15 ml [1 tbs]	10	neg
Parsley, fresh	25 g [1 oz]	5	neg
Parsnip, roast	25 g [1 oz]	30	½
Peas, raw	25 g [1 oz]	20	1
boiled	25 g [1 oz]	15	½
Peppers	one medium	20	neg
dried	25 g [1 oz]	110	neg
Pimento	25 g [1 oz]	5	neg
Potatoes			
boiled, old	25 g [1 oz]	25	1
boiled, new	25 g [1 oz]	20	1
chips, standard	25 g [1 oz]	70	2
crisps	25 g [1 oz]	150	2½
roast	25 g [1 oz]	45	1
baked, whole	175 g [6 oz]	150	1
Radish	25 g [1 oz]	5	neg
Spinach, boiled	25 g [1 oz]	10	neg
Spring onions	25 g [1 oz]	10	1
Sweetcorn, canned	25 g [1 oz]	20	1
whole cob	medium	85	9
Tomatoes, fresh	one medium	10	½
canned	75 g [3 oz]	15	½
juice	150 ml [½ pt]	20	1
ketchup	15 ml [1 tbs]	15	1
purée	15 ml [1 tbs]	10	½
Turnip, raw	25 g [1 oz]	5	½
Watercress	25 g [1 oz]	5	neg

INDEX